SIGNS, SYMBOLS & SYSTEMATICS

The ASE companion to 16–19 science

Members of the Working Party

Convenor

T. C. (Kit) Swinfen
Royal Society of Chemistry and late of Uppingham School, Rutland

Geoff Auty
Institute of Physics and New College, Pontefract, Yorks.

Martyn Berry
Royal Society of Chemistry and late of Chislehurst and Sidcup School, Kent

Phil Bunyan
General Inspector (Science), Notts.

Ben Faust
Royal Society of Chemistry and Loughborough Grammar School, Leics.

Richard Field
Institute of Electrical Engineers and Dulwich College, London

Chris King
Earth Science Teachers' Association and University of Keele Department of Education

Grace Monger
Institute of Biology and late of Holt School, Wokingham, Berks.

Dr Colin Osborne
Education Department, Royal Society of Chemistry

David H. Peet
Principal Professional Officer for Science, Cambridge International Examinations, UCLES

Nancy M. R. Reid
Earth Science Teachers' Association and Wyggeston and Queen Elizabeth I College, Leicester

Tim E. Watson
Institute of Physics and late of King's School Worcester

Dr Janet H. Webster
Subject Officer for Chemistry and Earth Sciences, Northern Examinations and Assessment Board

SIGNS,
SYMBOLS
&
SYSTEMATICS

The ASE companion to 16–19 science

Editor

T. C. (Kit) Swinfen

Permissions

The Association for Science Education have endeavoured to obtain permission for the use of copyrighted material and to express gratitude for this use. Any failure to do so is unwitting and if the attention of the ASE is brought to any such failure due acknowledgement will be made as soon as possible.

Table 3.2F.2: Data have been taken from *The Periodic Table Compendium* (The Royal Society of Chemistry 1994). Used with the permission of the Royal Society of Chemistry. Further details about the elements may be found at www.chemsoc.org/viselements.

Table 3.2F.3: Channel 4 Television (1991) *An A-Z of the elements*. Lide, David R. *The Handbook of Chemistry and Physics* © 1997 by David R. Lide. Reprinted by permission of CRC Press LLC.

Table 3.2M.2: Adapted from Phillips, W. O. and Chilton, T. J. (1994) *A-level Biology*. By permission of Oxford University Press.

Table 3.2M.3: Adapted from Larkcom, E., Adds, J. and Miller, R. (eds) (1996) *Nelson Advanced Modular Science: Cell biology and genetics*. Nelson.

Table 3.2M.4: Adapted from Monger, G. and Sangster, M. (1988) *Systematics and classification*. The Nuffield-Chelsea Curriculum Trust.

Table 3.2M.5: Adapted from Larkcom, E., Adds, J. and Miller, R. (eds) (1996) *Nelson Advanced Modular Science: The organism and the environment*. Nelson.

Table 3.2N.15: Adapted from Edwards, D. and King, C. (1999) *Geoscience: understanding geological processes*. Hodder and Stoughton.

Tables 3.2N.23 and 3.2N.24: Adapted from the Geology Development Team of the Northumberland Supported Self-Study Unit (1993) *The structure of the Earth*. Association for Science Education.

Section 11.4: Adapted from Institute of Biology (2000) *Biological nomenclature: standard terms and expressions used in the teaching of biology*. Ed. Alan Cadogan. 3rd edn. Institute of Biology.

Published by the Association for Science Education,
College Lane, Hatfield, Herts AL10 9AA

First published 2000

Printed by the Black Bear Press Ltd, Cambridge, UK

Designed and typeset by Paul and Hendrina Ellis

ISBN 0 86357 312 6

CONTENTS

Foreword

This is a companion to science for teachers of students aged 16–19, regardless of country (England, Northern Ireland, Scotland or Wales), institution (school, college, etc.) or course (A-level, AS-level, GNVQ, etc.). It replaces earlier ASE publications such as *Chemical nomenclature, symbols and terminology* and *SI units, signs, symbols and abbreviations*. It will, it is intended, be cited by Examination Boards as *the* sourcebook for science teaching at the 16–19 level.

This book aims to include all the factual information, within its remit, that teachers might need. It both covers, and gives standardisation for, biology, chemistry, electronics, Earth science and physics. Some chapters are informative rather than prescriptive. Chapter 8, the Glossary, gives information for the non-specialist, such as the chemist teaching a geology or soil science option or some GNVQ topics. Chapter 9, the Minefield, is written to stir the teacher into thinking clearly about some of the difficulties the beginner might have with what to the teacher are familiar concepts. ('We pay for the electricity we use.' Do we really?) Chapters 10 and 11 cover some mathematical topics of importance to science; they treat mathematics as the 'handmaid of science' rather than the 'Queen of sciences'.

There is a lot of information in this book. To help you locate items, the Contents list includes chapter and section titles and all the table titles. The Index is comprehensive but does not cover all the substances: look under inorganic compounds, organic compounds, polymers, rocks, etc.

The book stands alone: readers do not need to buy *Signs, symbols and systematics: The ASE companion to 5–16 science* as well. It includes much from the ASE publications named above. It takes into account various publications of the learned societies, and comments and advice from many people and organisations whose contribution is acknowledged below.

Acknowledgements

The Working Party is grateful for help and advice from many people. They include:
The Examination Boards of the UK (*co-ordinated by Dr Janet Webster*)
The Chemical Nomenclature Committee of the Royal Society of Chemistry (*co-ordinated by Dr Alan McNaught*)
Professor Ian Mills (*University of Reading*)
Dr Peter Borrows (*ASE Safeguards in Science Committee*)
David Sang (*author and editor, Bognor Regis*)
Professor D. Burns (*Queens University, Belfast*)
Professor Michael Brooks (*Geological Society*)
Kevin J. Thurlow (*Laboratory of the Government Chemist*)

Many other people, not named here, have made their contributions to the finished text and the Working Party thanks them for their help.

1 SI UNITS

1.1 SI units

'SI' stands for 'Système International d'Unités' or 'International System of Units'. The term 'SI System' is therefore incorrect. SI is a 'coherent' system based on seven *base units*.

Base units

metre	m	the unit of length
kilogram	kg	the unit of mass
second	s	the unit of time
ampere	A	the unit of electric current
kelvin	K	the unit of (thermodynamic) temperature difference
mole	mol	the unit of 'amount of substance'
candela	cd	the unit of luminous intensity

The *name* for a unit named after a person begins with a small letter (e.g. ampere); but the *symbol* for such a unit starts with a capital letter (e.g. A). (The one exception to this rule is the occasional use of L as a symbol for the litre because of the risk of confusion between the letter l and the numeral 1.)

All other SI units are derived from the base units by suitably multiplying or dividing one unit by one or more other units; they are called *derived units*. The units are 'coherent' when this multiplying and dividing is done without using any numerical factors. A coherent system is needed because the units used for measurement of physical quantities almost always depend on what has previously been defined. Only mass and time have units defined totally independently of all others.

When two or more symbols are combined to indicate a derived unit, a space or half space is inserted between them (e.g. N m, m s^{-1}).

No space is left between a prefix indicating powers of ten and the symbol to which it applies (e.g. mm, kg). This is very important to avoid confusion between m for metre and m for milli-, and in similar cases.

Derived units with special names

Many derived units have their own special names. For example, the ampere, A, is the base unit of current and the second, s, is the base unit of time. The derived unit of charge, the ampere second, A s, is called the coulomb, C. The derived units with special names used at the 16–19 level are as follows. (The units in parentheses are the base units from which the following are derived.)

Bq	**becquerel**	rate of activity (of radioactive source)	s^{-1}
C	**coulomb**	electric charge	A s
F	**farad**	capacitance	C V^{-1} (A^2 s^4 kg^{-1} m^{-2})
Gy	**gray**	absorbed dose of radiation	J kg^{-1} (m^2 s^{-2})
H	**henry**	electric inductance	Wb A^{-1} (kg m^2 A^{-2} s^{-2})
Hz	**hertz**	frequency	s^{-1}
J	**joule**	energy or work	N m (kg m^2 s^{-2})
N	**newton**	force	kg m s^{-2}
Ω	**ohm**	electric resistance	V A^{-1} (kg m^2 A^{-2} s^{-3})
Pa	**pascal**	pressure	N m^{-2} (kg m^{-1} s^{-2})
S	**siemens**	electric conductance	Ω^{-1} (A^2 s^3 kg^{-1} m^{-2})
Sv	**sievert**	equivalent dose of radiation	J kg^{-1} (m^2 s^{-2})
T	**tesla**	magnetic flux density	Wb m^{-2} (kg A^{-1} s^{-2})
V	**volt**	potential difference	J C^{-1} (kg m^2 A^{-1} s^{-3})
W	**watt**	power	J s^{-1} (kg m^2 s^{-3})
Wb	**weber**	magnetic flux	V s (kg m^2 A^{-1} s^{-2})

Multiples and sub-multiples of units may be constructed by the use of approved prefixes (see Section 1.3): for example, 0.001 V is more conveniently known as a millivolt, mV. The prefixes should normally be used so that the numeric part lies between 0.1 and 1000.

1.2 Definitions of SI base units

When the Metric System (the forerunner of the SI) was devised in Napoleonic France, the aim was to relate all units to the Earth as far as possible. The metre was originally defined as $\frac{1}{40\,000\,000}$ of the circumference of the Earth through Paris. For general use the international standard (or 'prototype') metre was made, being the distance between two marks on a platinum alloy bar held at Sèvres. Copies of this standard were held in other countries and there was a great deal of international calibration and cross-checking.

As far as possible SI units are now defined in terms of some physical quantity like the wavelength of light: this is reproducible anywhere in the world where the appropriate technology exists. Attempts to define mass in this way have so far not been successful.

METRE, m The metre is the unit of length: it is the length of the path travelled by light in vacuum during a time interval of $\frac{1}{299\,792\,458}$ of a second. Given the exact and fixed value for the speed of light, the length of the metre follows.

KILOGRAM, kg The kilogram is the unit of mass: it was originally the mass of one cubic decimetre of water. It is now defined as equal to the mass of the international prototype kilogram, held at the Bureau International des Poids et Mesures at Sèvres, France.

The kilogram, being a multiple of the gram, seems a strange choice for the name of a base unit. The initial selection of the gram (the mass of one cubic centimetre of water) conveniently suited the magnitudes of other units being used at the time and is even now more suitable for many small-scale laboratory experiments. The kilogram was found to be more suitable when creating a unified system of units for use throughout the whole of physics.

The spelling 'gram' rather than 'gramme' is accepted.

SECOND, s The second is the unit of time: it was originally defined as $\frac{1}{60\times24\times24}$ of the period of rotation of the Earth about its axis. We now know that this is not constant, though we still take one day as equal to $60 \times 60 \times 24$ seconds in our ordinary lives. The second is now defined as the duration of 9 192 631 770 periods of the radiation corresponding to the transition between the two hyperfine levels of the ground state of the caesium-133 atom.

AMPERE, A The ampere is the unit of electric current: it was originally taken as 'one coulomb per second' when the coulomb was the base unit. (It still is 1 C s^{-1}, but the coulomb is now defined in terms of the ampere and not the other way round.) The ampere is

defined in terms of the force between two wires. It is that constant current which, if maintained in two straight parallel conductors of infinite length, of negligible cross-section, and placed one metre apart in vacuum, would produce between these conductors a force equal to 2×10^{-7} newton per metre of length.

KELVIN, K The kelvin is the unit of thermodynamic temperature difference: it is $\frac{1}{273.16}$ of the thermodynamic temperature of the triple point of water. The kelvin is the same size as the degree Celsius.

MOLE, mol The mole is the unit of amount of substance: it is the amount of substance of a system which contains as many elementary entities as there are atoms of carbon in 0.012 kilogram of carbon-12. When the mole is used, the elementary entities must be specified and may be atoms, molecules, ions, electrons, other particles or specified groups of such particles. See also Section 9.2F.

CANDELA, cd The candela is the unit of luminous intensity: it is the luminous intensity, in a given direction, of a source that emits monochromatic radiation of frequency 540×10^{12} hertz and has a radiant intensity in that direction of $\frac{1}{683}$ watt per steradian.

Two units, formerly regarded as base units but now as 'dimensionless derived units', are:

RADIAN, rad The angle subtended by the arc of a circle which is equal in length to its radius. Strictly speaking this has no unit, since it is the ratio of two lengths, but 'rad' is often used to highlight that the angle is not being measured in degrees.

STERADIAN, sr The solid angle subtended at the centre of a sphere of radius r by an area of the surface of the sphere equal to r^2.

1.3 Prefixes

Multiples

deca-	10	**da**	(not used very much)
hecto-	100	**h**	(mainly used in 'hectare', a unit of area usually in the context of land. The 'are' is 100 m^2 and the hectare 10 000 m^2.)
kilo-	1000	**k**	
mega-	10^6	**M**	
giga-	10^9	**G**	
tera-	10^{12}	**T**	
peta-	10^{15}	**P**	
exa-	10^{18}	**E**	
zetta-	10^{21}	**Z**	
yotta-	10^{24}	**Y**	

Sub-multiples

deci-	$\frac{1}{10}$	**d**	(not used very much, except in cubic decimetre)
centi-	$\frac{1}{100}$	**c**	(not used much except in centisecond, centilitre and centimetre)
milli-	$\frac{1}{1000}$	**m**	
micro-	10^{-6}	**μ**	
nano-	10^{-9}	**n**	
pico-	10^{-12}	**p**	
femto-	10^{-15}	**f**	
atto-	10^{-18}	**a**	
zepto-	10^{-21}	**z**	
yocto-	10^{-24}	**y**	

Quantities can also be expressed in 'standard form', without using prefixes, e.g. '31 μV' can be written '3.1×10^{-5} V'.

2 PHYSICAL QUANTITIES, SYMBOLS AND UNITS

2.1 General introduction

Ideally there should be just one set of symbols to represent quantities and units with a letter symbol uniquely defined for each, and no duplication. Unfortunately there are insufficient letters available even when we use upper and lower case letters in both the English and the Greek alphabets.

2.1.1 Avoiding confusion and ambiguity

Where possible, letters represent the most obvious abbreviation (time, t; force, F, etc.) but this means that many letters have more than one use (mass m, metre m, milli- m). One method adopted to reduce confusion is that in printed information italic (sloping) script is used for quantity symbols (e.g. mass m) but Roman (upright) script is used for units (e.g. metre m) and for multiple indicators (e.g. m for milli-). In handwriting it is not usually possible to make this distinction.

In other instances, where a letter is very popular it is replaced by a less-used letter (e.g. I is used for electric current because c and c have so many uses). There is no good reason for the choice of I except that like many other choices of letter symbols it has become universally accepted through custom and practice. There are also situations where more than one symbol can be appropriate for the same basic concept. In particular 'length' has many different contexts in which it is measured, such as breadth, distance, radius, etc., so that l is not always the appropriate symbol. There is also a problem in some print styles of confusing the letter 'l' with the numeral '1', though there is less confusion in hand-written work.

A further restriction is that e is used for the base of natural logarithms (see Section 11.8) while d and δ have special meanings in calculus. Δ also has a special meaning, as has π in the context of circular measurements. Σ is used to denote a summing operation. These Greek letters are hardly ever used to denote quantities.

As a consequence, a set of recommended symbols cannot be absolute. Much depends on the context and the branch of science under consideration. The main thing is to avoid confusion or ambiguity. It is therefore good practice in any calculation or mathematical proof to define the symbols being used. The symbols for quantities (which are in italics) are in the final analysis at the choice of the user. Symbols for units (roman) are mandatory – the correct symbol must be used.

In many instances understanding of concepts is promoted by the choice of units (e.g. m s^{-1} for speed shows that distance divided by time is the appropriate calculation to find this quantity). For some derived units special names exist. Those used in 16–19 science are listed in Section 1.1. Sometimes the name is used because of common practice (e.g. W for power rather than J s^{-1}) but in other situations it can be to avoid complexity (e.g. N for force replacing kg m s^{-2}).

2.1.2 Concepts with no unit

The most obvious type of concept with no unit is that in which the quantity is the ratio of two quantities which are themselves measured in the same units (e.g. refractive index or coefficient of friction). No unit of any kind can be stated or considered. In the tables following, the symbol *r is used to imply a ratio of this kind.

Some dimensionless quantities (e.g. order of diffraction) are always integers. These are denoted by *d.

The situation is not always as clear as this.

The radian is an angle measure found by the division of two specified lengths. Although this gives rise to a unitless quantity, the detailed specification of the two lengths to be used means that the name 'radian' should still be used. For the functions 'sine', 'cosine', etc., two lengths are again divided in relation to an angle but the result is regarded as purely numerical. It is not an angle and the use of the abbreviations 'sin', 'cos', etc., are sufficient to make clear what is meant.

Another unitless quantity is 'number of revolutions'. Like 'number of coils' it is a numerical count of repeated events. Even so it is possible to have a fractional count – unlike 'number of molecules', which is a digital quantity. For all of these it would be much clearer to specify the name of what has been counted rather than leave the student to work it out.

2.1.3   A provocative note

The very name 'unit' suggests that just one of a kind of item is under consideration for measurement. So a letter should not be added to the end of the name of a unit to imply a plural amount. For example:

> The length is 3 metre (not 3 metres)

> The speed is 4 metre per second (not 4 metres per second)

In speech it is almost impossible to avoid the use of the extra 's' and in continuous written prose the writer must use a certain amount of discretion so that what is written sounds accurate without being over-pedantic. A full stop is not written after the symbol for a unit except where it occurs in the ordinary way at the end of a sentence.

2.2   Physical quantities and units

In the tables following, physical quantities and units are treated in the order:

A   Length and time
B   Motion, mass and force
C   Changing direction
D   Energy
E   Heat
F   Molecular properties
G   Chemical reactions
H   Material properties
I   Electricity
J   Electric and magnetic fields
K   Electrochemistry
L   Sound
M   Biology
N   Earth science

Within these broad headings the order of the list of recommended symbols for physical quantities together with their units and abbreviations is as far as possible the order of development of derived concepts from basic ones. Due to the way in which concepts in physics are interlinked, however, there can not be a single or 'correct' way to present this information and the order may perhaps appear somewhat arbitrary.

Most of the units stated are defined by SI but a few non-SI units are quoted because they are in common use.

Comments are given at the bottom of the relevant table.

Chapters 3, 8 and 9 use these same letters, to aid cross-referencing.

2.2A   Length and time

Quantity name	Symbol	SI unit name	SI unit symbol	Other units used, or comments
length	l	metre	m	mm, cm, km
breadth	b			
thickness (depth)	d			
height	h			
radius	r			
diameter	d			
distance (along a path)	s			
in geometry/trigonometry	a, b, c			
vertical displacement	y			
horizontal displacement	x			
in 3rd dimension	z			
separation	s			
(of slits or gratings)				
distance from sources to observed pattern	D			
slit width (aperture)	a			
fringe separation	w			
amplitude (of vibrations)	A			
wavelength	λ			
focal length	f			
object distance	u			
image distance	v			
area	A, S	square metre	m^2	cm^2, mm^2 (1)

Quantity name	Symbol	SI unit name	SI unit symbol	Other units used, or comments
volume	V	cubic metre	m^3	cm^3 dm^3 (= litre, l or L), ml or mL
time	t	second	s	ms, μs minute, hour, day, and year (non-SI)
period (time period)	T			
time constant	τ			
half-life (radioactivity)	$t_{\frac{1}{2}}$			
frequency	f	hertz	Hz	
rate of rotation (rotational frequency)	n	hertz per second	Hz s^{-1}	rev. per minute (2)

(1) S is used in the particular context of *surface* area as an alternative to A.

(2) Although the 'number of revolutions' is a non-dimensional number, the inclusion of the word 'revolution' may make the situation clearer in some work. Revolution per second appears sensible, but revolution hertz does not.

2.2B   Motion, mass and force

Quantity name	Symbol	SI unit name	SI unit symbol	Other units used, or comments
speed, velocity	v, u	metre per second	$m\ s^{-1}$	$km\ h^{-1}$
speed of sound	c			
speed of electromagnetic waves (light)	c			
velocity of molecule	c			
perpendicular components	u, v, w			
average speed of molecules	$\bar{c}, \bar{u}$			
root mean square speed of molecules	$c_{rms}, \sqrt{\overline{c^2}}$			
acceleration	a	metre per second squared	$m\ s^{-2}$	
acceleration due to gravity (acceleration of free fall)	g			
mass	m	kilogram	kg	gram, g; milligram, mg tonne (1000 kg) (1)
momentum	p	newton second kilogram metre per second squared	N s $kg\ m\ s^{-2}$	(2)
impulse	p			
coefficient of restitution	e	no unit (*r)		
force	F	newton	N	(3)
weight	W			
tension/thrust	T			
reaction (normal)	R			
push/pull	P			
gravitational field strength	g	newton per kilogram	$N\ kg^{-1}$	

Quantity name	Symbol	SI unit name	SI unit symbol	Other units used, or comments
universal constant of gravitation	G	newton metre squared per kilogram squared	$N\ m^2\ kg^{-2}$	
pressure	p	pascal	Pa	kPa bar (= 100 kPa) mbar (= 100 Pa) atmosphere = atm (= 101.325 kPa) also Torr, mmHg

(1) M is used for mass only if it is clearly a very large mass, e.g. mass of Earth in gravity calculations, otherwise use m_1, m_2, etc.

(2) Momentum and impulse are often represented by the product mv to avoid confusion with other uses of p.

(3) F is preferred for force in most dynamic situations but the use of additional letters, particularly those listed, and with the implications given, may be more appropriate for problems in statics.

2.2C Changing direction

Quantity name	Symbol	SI unit name	SI unit symbol	Other units used, or comments
moment of a force torque, couple	T, M T or G	newton metre	N m	(1), (2)

angle
 	
angle of incidence
  of reflection /refraction
critical angle
 	
refracting angle of prism
angle of deviation
  of minimum deviation
angle of rotation for
  polarised light
phase angle
	$\theta, \phi, \alpha,$
	β, γ, ψ
	i
	r
	c or i_c
	
	A
	D
	D_{min}
	α
	
	ϕ
		radian	rad	degree, °
				
				or use i_1, i_2, especially in two different media
				(use of c invites confusion with the speed of light)

angular velocity angular frequency	ω w	radian per second	$rad\ s^{-1}$	(3)
angular acceleration	a	radian per second squared	$rad\ s^{-2}$	
angular momentum	L	newton metre second	N m s	(4)
moment of inertia	I	kilogram metre squared	$kg\ m^2$	

refractive index
refractive index of material
  A relative to a vacuum
relative refractive index
  of medium A to medium B
	n
	n_A
	
	$_A n_B$
		no unit (*r)		

power of a lens	P	dioptre (metre^{-1})	D	
magnification angular magnification dispersive power	m M w	no unit (*r) no unit (*r) no unit (*r)		

Quantity name	Symbol	SI unit name	SI unit symbol	Other units used, or comments
order of diffraction	n	no unit (*d)		

(1) Since the force and the distance are perpendicular, the newton metre here is not the same as the joule.

(2) T is preferred to depict all turning effects, including static problems involving the principle of moments.

(3) This is the term in simple harmonic motion being $2\pi f$ where f (in Hz) is the frequency of oscillation. Although the motion is in a straight line, not circular, there is always a synchronous circular motion (real or imaginary) so that measurement in radian per second gives the appropriate magnitude for this concept.

(4) The product $I\omega$ is commonly used.

2.2D   Energy

Quantity name	Symbol	SI unit name	SI unit symbol	Other units used, or comments
work	W	joule	J	kJ
energy	E	joule	J	kJ
				kilowatt hour, kW h
				electronvolt, eV
potential energy	E_p			(1)
kinetic energy	E_k			(1)
heat	Q			
internal energy	U			
electrical energy	W			(2)
power	P	watt	W	kW
efficiency	E or η	no unit (*r)		(3)
Planck constant	h	joule second	J s	

(1) P.E. and K.E. can be used as abbreviations at the start of a calculation but not as algebraic symbols within a calculation.

(2) W (implying *work* as an alternative to energy) is generally used in electrical calculations because E and ε have other uses in electrical topics.

(3) Efficiency is a figure between 0 and 1 but is often expressed as a percentage. The symbol is a hand-written capital E, not a Greek epsilon. The use of η overcomes this problem.

2.2E   Heat

Quantity name	Symbol	SI unit name	SI unit symbol	Other units used, or comments
temperature (common)	θ			(1) degree Celsius, °C
thermodynamic (absolute) temperature	T	kelvin	K	
temperature difference	$\Delta\theta, \Delta T$			
critical temperature	T_c			
heat capacity	C	joule per kelvin	J K^{-1}	
specific heat capacity	c	joule per kilogram kelvin	J kg^{-1} K^{-1}	kJ kg^{-1} K^{-1}
specific heat capacity at constant pressure	c_p			
specific heat capacity at constant volume	c_v			

Quantity name	Symbol	SI unit name	SI unit symbol	Other units used, or comments
molar heat capacity at constant pressure at constant volume	C_p C_v	joule per mole kelvin	J mol^{-1} K^{-1}	
ratio of principal specific heat capacities C_p/C_v	γ	no unit (*r)		
latent heat specific latent heat	L l	joule joule per kilogram	J J kg^{-1}	kJ kg^{-1} (2)
enthalpy enthalpy of reaction specific enthalpy change calorific value of foodstuffs, see 2.2M	H ΔH ΔH	joule joule per mole joule per kilogram	J J mol^{-1} J kg^{-1}	kJ kJ mol^{-1}
entropy	S	joule per kelvin	J K^{-1}	
activation energy	E_a	joule per mole	J mol^{-1}	kJ mol^{-1}
rate of conduction of heat	p, H	watt	W	(3)
thermal conductivity	$\lambda\ (k)$	watt per metre kelvin	W m^{-1} K^{-1}	(4)
U-value	U	watt per metre squared kelvin	W m^{-2} K^{-1}	(5)
Stefan constant (Stefan–Boltzmann)	σ	watt per metre^2 kelvin^4	W m^{-2} K^{-4}	
linear expansivity cubic expansivity	α γ	per kelvin per kelvin	K^{-1} K^{-1}	
emissivity	ε	no unit (*r)		
absorption factor reflection factor transmission factor	α ρ τ	no unit (*r)		

(1) Celsius remains popular for everyday temperature measurements.

(2) Hand-written (or italic) small l should always be used, to avoid confusion with a figure 1.

(3) Rate of flow of heat energy is a power measurement. Hence use p or H in preference to a symbol implying 'flow'.

(4) λ is already heavily used, so k is preferable.

(5) U-value is a thermal conductivity for a particular thickness of material, including compound layers.

2.2F Molecular properties

Quantity name	Symbol	SI unit name	SI unit symbol	Other units used, or comments
number of molecules	N	no unit (*d) (molecules)		(1)
number density of molecules	n	(molecules) per cubic metre	m^{-3}	(1)
universal gas constant (molar)	R	joule per mole kelvin	J mol^{-1} K^{-1}	

Quantity name	Symbol	SI unit name	SI unit symbol	Other units used, or comments
gas constant per unit mass	r	joule per kilogram	$J\ kg^{-1}\ K^{-1}$	
Boltzmann constant	k	joule per kelvin	$J\ K^{-1}$	
Avogadro constant	N_A, L	per mole	mol^{-1}	(1) (2)
molar volume	V_m	cubic metre per mole	$m^3\ mol^{-1}$	
specific volume	v	cubic metre per kilogram	$m^3\ kg^{-1}$	
proton number (atomic number) nucleon number (mass number) neutron number	Z A N	no units		
amount of substance	n	mole	mol	mmol
molar mass	M	kilogram per mole	$kg\ mol^{-1}$	$g\ mol^{-1}$
relative atomic mass relative molecular mass	A_r M_r	no units (*r)		
mass of molecule of electron of proton of neutron of atom	m m_e m_p m_n m_a	kilogram	kg	g

(1) 'Molecule' is a counted number (hence dimensionless) but it makes some sense to refer to what is counted in some features of description.

(2) L is already well used, so N_A is preferable.

2.2G   Chemical reactions

Quantity name	Symbol	SI unit name	SI unit symbol	Other units used, or comments
mole fraction of substance B	x_B	no units (*r)		
concentration of substance B	c_B or [B]			mole per cubic decimetre, $mol\ dm^{-3}$ (1)
mass concentration of solute B	ρ_B			gram per cubic decimetre, $g\ dm^{-3}$ (1)
solubility of substance B		kilogram per cubic metre	$kg\ m^{-3}$	also $mol\ dm^{-3}$, $g\ dm^{-3}$ (1) $g/100\ cm^3$ of solvent

Quantity name	Symbol	SI unit name	SI unit symbol	Other units used, or comments
rate constant	k	units depend on the order of the reaction		
order of reaction		*r		
molecularity of reaction		*d		
equilibrium constant	K	units depend on the equilibrium considered		
(concentration basis)	K_c	units depend on the equilibrium considered		
(pressure basis)	K_p	units depend on the equilibrium considered		
solubility product	K_{sp}	units depend on the equilibrium considered		
acidity constant	K_a	mol dm^{-3}		
basicity constant	K_b	mol dm^{-3}		
ionic product for water	K_w	mol^2 dm^{-6}		
pH		*r		
pK_a		*r		
pK_b		*r		
pK_w		*r		
osmotic pressure	Π	Pa		kPa, MPa

(1) The volume is that of the solution, not of the solvent taken. See Section 9.2G.

2.2H   Material properties

Quantity name	Symbol	SI unit name	SI unit symbol	Other units used, or comments
density (volumic mass)	ρ	kilogram per cubic metre	kg m^{-3}	g cm^{-3}
mass per unit length (lineic mass)	μ	kilogram per metre	kg m^{-1}	
stress (tensile/compressive)	σ	pascal	Pa	
strain (linear)	ε	no unit (*r)		
Young modulus	E	pascal	Pa	kN mm^{-2}, mPa, GPa
shear stress	τ	newton per metre squared	Pa	kN mm^{-2}, mPa, GPa
shear strain	γ	radian	rad	
shear modulus (rigidity modulus)	G	newton per metre squared	Pa	kN mm^{-2}, mPa, GPa
bulk modulus	K	pascal	Pa	kN mm^{-2}, mPa, GPa
compressibility	κ	per pascal	Pa^{-1}	
surface tension	γ	newton per metre	N m^{-1}	(1)
surface energy	γ	joule per metre squared	J m^{-2}	(1)
viscosity (coefficient of viscosity)	η	newton second per metre squared	N s m^{-2}	
Reynolds number	Re	no unit (*r)		

Quantity name	Symbol	SI unit name	SI unit symbol	Other units used, or comments
coefficient of friction	μ	no unit (*r)		
radioactive decay constant	λ	per second	s^{-1}	
activity (of radioactive source)	A	becquerel (= per second)	$Bq\ (= s^{-1})$	(2), (3)
absorbed dose of radiation	D	gray	$Gy\ (= J\ kg^{-1})$	(2), (4)
equivalent dose of radiation	H	sievert	$Sv\ (= J\ kg^{-1})$	(2), (5)

(1) These units are equivalent, which explains why the same symbol is used to represent these two slightly different concepts.

(2) These units all have equivalent existing SI units as shown but these names are used to indicate the special context in which the measurement is applied.

(3) The curie = 3.70×10^{10} Bq.

(4) The rad = 0.01 Gy.

(5) The equivalent dose, H, is a measure of the damage to the body. The rem = 0.01 Sv.

$$\frac{\text{equivalent dose}}{\text{Sv}} = \frac{\text{absorbed dose}}{\text{Gy}} \times \text{relative biological effectiveness (r.b.e.)}$$

i.e. $\dfrac{H}{Sv} = \dfrac{D}{Gy} \times$ r.b.e.

The 'relative biological effectiveness' is a factor indicating the relative damage to human tissue associated with the equal release of energy caused by different ionising radiations. For α-particles it is taken as 10; for medium-energy β-particles and γ-photons it is usually taken as 1.

2.2I   Electricity

Quantity name	Symbol	SI unit name	SI unit symbol	Other units used, or comments
current peak current in ac root mean square current initial current in charge/discharge etc.	I I_0 I_{rms} I_0	ampere (amp)	A	mA, μA (1)
current density	J	ampere per square metre	$A\ m^{-2}$	
charge	$Q, (q)$	coulomb	$C\ (= A\ s)$	(2)
specific charge	q	coulomb per kilogram	$C\ kg^{-1}$	
elementary charge	e	coulomb	C	(3)
surface density of charge	σ	coulomb per square metre	$C\ m^{-2}$	
charge density (volumic charge)	ρ	coulomb per cubic metre	$C\ m^{-3}$	

Quantity name	Symbol	SI unit name	SI unit symbol	Other units used, or comments
potential difference, pd	$V, U, \Delta Q$	volt	V	(4)
potential	V			
electromotive force	E			(4)
peak potential, emf in ac	V_0, E_0			
root mean square potential, emf	V_{rms}, E_{rms}			
work function	ϕ			
resistance	R	ohm	Ω	
resistivity	ρ	ohm metre	Ω m	
electrical conductance	G	siemens	$S = \Omega^{-1}$	
electrical conductivity	$\sigma \; (\gamma)$	siemens per metre	$S \; m^{-1}$	(5)
reactance	X	ohm	Ω	
inductive reactance	X_L			
capacitive reactance	X_C			
impedance	Z			
capacitance	C	farad	F	

(1) I_0, V_0 and Q_0 are all maximum values, whether it be ac or charging/discharging.

(2) Q should be used for charge wherever possible. q is only appropriate if it is a small charge in comparison with other charged surroundings, e.g. a charged body moving between, but not landing on, charged plates. If the moving charge adds to the charge of the plates then the use of ΔQ will probably be more appropriate.

(3) Charge on electron = $-e$.

(4) Potential difference and electromotive force are such long and cumbersome titles that pd and emf have become universal replacements. However the situation remains unsatisfactory to the extent that 'voltage' is often used in electronics and in electrical engineering and is almost the only case where the name of the unit dictates an acceptable name for the concept (though mileage and footage are often used colloquially). See Section 9.2l.

(5) γ fits better with G to match ρ with R in comparable formulae. Is the recent change to σ perhaps to remind us to use the siemens?

2.2J Electric and magnetic fields

Quantity name	Symbol	SI unit name	SI unit symbol	Other units used, or comments
electric field strength	E	volt per metre	$V \; m^{-1}$	(1)
		newton per coulomb	$N \; C^{-1}$	
electric dipole moment	μ	coulomb metre	C m	
permittivity	ε	farad per metre	$F \; m^{-1}$	
permittivity of free space	ε_0			
relative permittivity	ε_r	no unit (*r)		
magnetic flux density	B	tesla	T	
magnetic flux	Φ	weber	Wb	
magnetic field strength	H	amp turn per metre	$A \; turn \; m^{-1}$	(2)
		or amp per metre	or $A \; m^{-1}$	
magnetic flux linkage	$N \Phi$	weber turn	Wb turn	(3)
permeability	μ	henry per metre	$H \; m^{-1}$	
permeability of free space	μ_0			

Quantity name	Symbol	SI unit name	SI unit symbol	Other units used, or comments
relative permeability	μ_r	no units (*r)		
number of turns of a coil	N	turn		(4)
number of turns per unit length (turn density)	n	turn per metre or per metre		(4)
self inductance	L	henry	H	
mutual inductance	M			

(1) These two units are equivalent. N C^{-1} is appropriate to the definition of field strength but V m^{-1} is more useful when intending to take measurements. Potential gradient is an alternative concept using the same unit.

(2) The word 'turn' is not necessary here as it is a non-dimensional number by which the other figures must be multiplied to arrive at the correct magnitude. However, its inclusion may help to clarify what has been done.

(3) The word 'turn' can hardly be avoided here despite its non-dimensional quality.

(4) See other comments on non-dimensional numbers (of turns).

2.2K Electrochemistry

Quantity name	Symbol	SI unit name	SI unit symbol	Other units used, or comments
charge number (for an ion B)	z_B	no unit (*d)		
Faraday constant	F	coulomb per mole	C mol^{-1}	
standard electrode potential	E^o or $E^{\ominus}$	volt	V	

2.2L Sound

Quantity name	Symbol	SI unit name	SI unit symbol	Other units used, or comments
sound intensity	I	watt per square metre	W m^{-2}	decibel dB ($= 10^{-12}$ W m^{-2}) see Sections 3.2L, 8.2L and 9.2L

2.2M Biology

Quantity name	Symbol	SI unit name	SI unit symbol	Other units used, or comments
calorific value of foods		joule	J	kJ, MJ (may also be expressed as J kg^{-1} (etc.) or J (other mass)$^{-1}$, according to context (1)
water potential	ψ	pascal	Pa	kPa, MPa

(1) Calorific values of foodstuffs are still sometimes expressed in calories or Calories. The 'calorie' is the quantity of heat energy required to raise the temperature of one gram of water from 14.5 °C to 15.5 °C. The Calorie, or kilocalorie, is 1000 times this. The possibilities of confusion between calorie and Calorie are obvious. The Working Party recommends that whenever possible these units should not be used.

2.2N Earth science

Quantity name	Symbol	SI unit name	SI unit symbol	Other units used, or comments
gravitational field strength	g	newton per kilogram	$N\ kg^{-1}$	
heat flux	J or q	watt per square metre	$W\ m^{-2}$	$mW\ m^{-2}$
magnetic anomaly		tesla	T	nanotesla, nT
mineral hardness		Mohs' scale units	no units	
mass fraction (small) or volume fraction (small)		part per billion parts per million parts per thousand (permille – various spellings)	ppb ppm $^{0}/_{00}$	$= 10^{-9}$ $= 10^{-6}$ $= 10^{-3}$
particle diameters	d	metre ϕ units	m	mm, pm ($\phi = \log[\text{diameter/mm}]$)
permeability		metre per second	$m\ s^{-1}$	metre per day, m/day
relative density			no unit (*r)	
rock strength		pascal	Pa	megapascal, MPa
time	t	year	a	million years, Ma thousand million years, Ga

3 CONSTANTS AND DATA

3.1 General introduction

Most of the information in this Chapter applies to Earth science. There are several data books on the market covering the needs of syllabuses in physics and chemistry for the 16–19 age range, but information is less easily available for Earth science.

3.1.1 Fundamental constants

These are given to 4 significant figures where there is experimental uncertainty.

Constant	Symbol	Value	Notes
speed of light in a vacuum	c_0	299 792 458 m s^{-1}	(defined exactly)
electron rest mass	m_e	9.110×10^{-31} kg	
proton rest mass	m_p	1.673×10^{-27} kg	
neutron rest mass	m_n	1.675×10^{-27} kg	
standard atmosphere	atm	1.013×10^5 N m^{-2}	
Planck constant	h	6.626×10^{-34} J s	
Rydberg constant	R_∞	1.097×10^5 cm^{-1}	
Boltzmann constant	k	1.381×10^{-23} J K^{-1}	
gas constant	R	8.315 J K^{-1} mol^{-1}	
zero of the Celsius scale		273.15 K	
atomic mass constant	m_u	1.661×10^{-27} kg	
Avogadro constant	L, N_A	6.022×10^{23} mol^{-1}	
molar volume of ideal gas		22.71 dm^3 mol^{-1} (1 bar, 273.15 K)	
elementary charge	e	1.602×10^{-19} C	
Faraday constant	F	9.649×10^4 C mol^{-1}	
ratio of circumference to diameter of circle	π	3.142	(these can be calculated to an
base of natural logarithms	e	2.718	infinite number of figures:
natural logarithm of 10	$\ln_{10}$	2.303	quoted to four here)

3.2 Physical and chemical data

In this section, the physical and chemical data are treated in the same order as in Chapter 2 (see list below).

A Length and time
B Motion, mass and force
C Changing direction
D Energy
E Heat
F Molecular properties
G Chemical reactions
H Material properties
I Electricity
J Electric and magnetic fields
K Electrochemistry
L Sound
M Biology
N Earth science

3.2F Molecular properties   3.2F.1 Periodic Table

1	2	3	4	5	6	7	8	9	10	11	12	13	14	15	16	17	18
H 1 Hydrogen																	**He** 2 Helium
Li 3 Lithium	**Be** 4 Beryllium											**B** 5 Boron	**C** 6 Carbon	**N** 7 Nitrogen	**O** 8 Oxygen	**F** 9 Fluorine	**Ne** 10 Neon
Na 11 Sodium	**Mg** 12 Magnesium											**Al** 13 Aluminium	**Si** 14 Silicon	**P** 15 Phosphorus	**S** 16 Sulfur	**Cl** 17 Chlorine	**Ar** 18 Argon
K 19 Potassium	**Ca** 20 Calcium	**Sc** 21 Scandium	**Ti** 22 Titanium	**V** 23 Vanadium	**Cr** 24 Chromium	**Mn** 25 Manganese	**Fe** 26 Iron	**Co** 27 Cobalt	**Ni** 28 Nickel	**Cu** 29 Copper	**Zn** 30 Zinc	**Ga** 31 Gallium	**Ge** 32 Germanium	**As** 33 Arsenic	**Se** 34 Selenium	**Br** 35 Bromine	**Kr** 36 Krypton
Rb 37 Rubidium	**Sr** 38 Strontium	**Y** 39 Yttrium	**Zr** 40 Zirconium	**Nb** 41 Niobium	**Mo** 42 Molybdenum	**Tc** 43 Technetium	**Ru** 44 Ruthenium	**Rh** 45 Rhodium	**Pd** 46 Palladium	**Ag** 47 Silver	**Cd** 48 Cadmium	**In** 49 Indium	**Sn** 50 Tin	**Sb** 51 Antimony	**Te** 52 Tellurium	**I** 53 Iodine	**Xe** 54 Xenon
Cs 55 Caesium	**Ba** 56 Barium	**La** 57 Lanthanum	**Hf** 72 Hafnium	**Ta** 73 Tantalum	**W** 74 Tungsten	**Re** 75 Rhenium	**Os** 76 Osmium	**Ir** 77 Iridium	**Pt** 78 Platinum	**Au** 79 Gold	**Hg** 80 Mercury	**Tl** 81 Thallium	**Pb** 82 Lead	**Bi** 83 Bismuth	**Po** 84 Polonium	**At** 85 Astatine	**Rn** 86 Radon
Fr 87 Francium	**Ra** 88 Radium	**Ac** 89 Actinium	**Rf** 104 Rutherfordium	**Db** 105 Dubnium	**Sg** 106 Seaborgium	**Bh** 107 Bohrium	**Hs** 108 Hassium	**Mt** 109 Meitnerium									

s-block · d-block · p-block

f-block

Ce 58 Cerium	**Pr** 59 Praseodymium	**Nd** 60 Neodymium	**Pm** 61 Promethium	**Sm** 62 Samarium	**Eu** 63 Europium	**Gd** 64 Gadolinium	**Tb** 65 Terbium	**Dy** 66 Dysprosium	**Ho** 67 Holmium	**Er** 68 Erbium	**Tm** 69 Thulium	**Yb** 70 Ytterbium	**Lu** 71 Lutetium
Th 90 Thorium	**Pa** 91 Protactinium	**U** 92 Uranium	**Np** 93 Neptunium	**Pu** 94 Plutonium	**Am** 95 Americium	**Cm** 96 Curium	**Bk** 97 Berkelium	**Cf** 98 Californium	**Es** 99 Einsteinium	**Fm** 100 Fermium	**Md** 101 Mendelevium	**No** 102 Nobelium	**Lr** 103 Lawrencium

3.2F.2   Selected data for the elements

Name	Symbol	Atomic number Z	Relative atomic mass A_r	Melting point/K	Boiling point/K	History and derivation of name
actinium	Ac	89	227*	1320	3470	(Gk *aktinos* = ray) Discovered in uranium minerals in 1899 in Paris, France, by A. Debierne.
aluminium	Al	13	27.0	936	2740	(Lat *alumen* = alum) Discovered (impure) in 1825 in Copenhagen, Denmark, by H. C. Oersted.
americium	Am	95	243*	1267	2880	(America = country where discovered) Discovered after the neutron bombardment of plutonium in 1944 in Chicago, USA, by G. T. Seaborg and co-workers.
antimony	Sb	51	121.8	904	2023	(Gk *anti monos* = not alone) Known since 17th century and probably from Middle Ages.
argon	Ar	18	39.9	83.8	87.3	(Gk *argos* = inactive) Discovered in air in 1894 in London by Lord Rayleigh and Sir William Ramsey.
arsenic	As	33	74.9	(amorphous) 889		(Gk *arsenikos* = yellow orpiment) Discovered in 300 in China by Ko Hung, *element* first obtained in 1649.
astatine	At	85	210*	575	610	(Gk *astatos* = unstable) Discovered after the alpha bombardment of bismuth in 1940 in California, USA, by D. R. Corson and co-workers.
barium	Ba	56	137.3	983	2023	(Gk *barys* = heavy) Discovered in 1808 in London by Sir Humphrey Davy.
berkelium	Bk	97	247*	n/a	n/a	(Berkeley = university where discovered) Discovered after the neutron bombardment of plutonium in 1949 in California, USA, by S. G. Thompson and co-workers.
beryllium	Be	4	9.0	1551	3243	(Gk *beryllos* = beryl) Metal isolated in 1797 in Paris, France, by Nicholas Vauquelin (and independently by A. Bussey).
bismuth	Bi	83	209.0	545	1833	(Lat *bisemutum* = Ger weisse masse = white mass) Known since 15th century. Discovered in 1450 by B. Valentine.
bohrium	Bh	107	n/a*	n/a	n/a	(= Niels Bohr) USSR 1976, Germany 1981.
boron	B	5	10.8	2573	3931	(Arabic *buraq* = borax) Discovered in 1808 in London by Sir Humphrey Davy and in Paris, France, by L. J. Lussac and L. J. Thenard.
bromine	Br	35	79.9	265.9	332	(Gk *bromos* = stench) Discovered in 1826 in Montpelier, France, by A. J. Balard.
cadmium	Cd	48	112.4	594	1038	(Lat *cadmia* = calamine) Discovered in 1817 in Gottingen, Germany, by F. Stromeyer (and independently by K. Hermann and J. Roloff).

(* = radioactive)

Name	Symbol	Atomic number Z	Relative atomic mass A_r	Melting point/K	Boiling point/K	History and derivation of name
caesium	Cs	55	132.9	301.6	952	(Lat *caesius* = sky blue) Discovered in 1860 in Heidelberg, Germany, by R. Bunsen and G. R. Kirchoff (and independently by Klaproth).
calcium	Ca	20	40.1	1112	1757	(Lat *calx* = lime) Discovered in 1808 in London by Sir Humphrey Davy.
californium	Cf	98	251*	1173 (est)	n/a	(California = state where discovered) Discovered after the neutron bombardment of plutonium in 1950 in California, USA, by S. G. Thompson and co-workers.
carbon	C	6	12.011 ^{12}C =12.000	4100 under pressure (diamond)	5100	(Lat *carbo* = charcoal) Diamond and graphite known from prehistoric times. C_{60} discovered in 1985 by H. Kroto and R. E. Smalley in Texas, USA.
cerium	Ce	58	140.1	1072	3699	(Ceres = an asteroid discovered in 1801) Discovered in 1803 in Vestmandland, Sweden, by J. J. Berzelius and W. Hisinger.
chlorine	Cl	17	35.5	172.2	239	(Gk *chloros* = pale green) Discovered in 1774 in Uppsala, Sweden, by C. W. Scheele (but first recognised as an element in 1810 in London by Sir Humphrey Davy).
chromium	Cr	24	52.0	2130	2755	(Gk *chroma* = colour) Discovered in 1797 in Paris, France, by Nicholas Vanquelin.
cobalt	Co	27	58.9	1768	3143	(Ger *Kobold* = goblin) Discovered in 1735 in Stockholm, Sweden, by G. Brandt.
copper	Cu	29	63.5	1357	2840	(Lat *cuprum* = Cyprus) Known for more than 5000 years.
curium	Cm	96	247*	1610	n/a	(= Pierre and Marie Curie) Discovered after neutron bombardment of plutonium in 1944 in California, USA, by G. T. Seaborg and co-workers.
dubnium	Db	105	n/a*	n/a	n/a	(= Dubna laboratory, Russia) Claimed in 1967 Dubna, 1970 Berkeley, USA
dysprosium	Dy	66	162.5	1685	2835	(Gk *dysprositos* = hard to get) Discovered in 1886 in Paris, France, by P. E. Lecoq de Boisbaudron.
einsteinium	Es	99	254*	n/a	n/a	(= Albert Einstein) Discovered in the debris of the thermo-nuclear explosion at Eniwetok, in the Pacific, in 1952 by G. R. Choppin and co-workers.
erbium	Er	68	167.3	1802	3136	(Swedish town Ytterby = source of mineral) Discovered in 1843 in Stockholm, Sweden, by C. G. Mosander.
europium	Eu	63	152.0	1095	1870	(= Europe) Discovered in 1901 in Paris, France, by E. A. Demarcay.

(* = radioactive)

Name	Symbol	Atomic number Z	Relative atomic mass A_r	Melting point/K	Boiling point/K	History and derivation of name
fermium	Fm	100	257*	n/a	n/a	(= Enrico Fermi) Discovered in the debris of the thermo-nuclear explosion at Eniwetok, in the Pacific, in 1952 by G. R. Choppin and co-workers.
fluorine	F	9	19.0	54	85	(Lat *fluere* = to flow) Discovered in 1886 in Paris, France, by H. Moissan.
francium	Fr	87	223*	300	950	(= France) Discovered in 1939 in Paris, France, by Marguerite Perey.
gadolinium	Gd	64	157.3	1586	3539	(= J. Gadolin, Finnish chemist) Discovered in 1880 in Geneva, Switzerland, by J. C. Galissard de Marignac.
gallium	Ga	31	69.7	303	2676	(Lat *Gallia* = France) Discovered in 1875 in Paris, France, by P. E. Lecoq de Boisbaudron. (Properties predicted by D. Mendeleev, who called it ekaaluminium.)
germanium	Ge	32	72.6	1211	3103	(Lat *Germanium* = Germany) Discovered in 1886 in Freiberg, Germany, by C. A. Winkler. (Properties predicted by D. Mendeleev, who called it ekasilicon.)
gold	Au	79	197.0	1338	3080	(Anglo-Saxon 'gold') Known since prehistoric times.
hafnium	Hf	72	178.5	2503	5470	(Lat *Hafnia* = Copenhagen) Discovered in 1923 in Copenhagen, Denmark, by D. Coster and G. C. von Hevesey.
hassium	Hs	108	n/a*	n/a	n/a	(Lat *Hassia* = the German state Hesse, in the capital of which, Darmstadt, the element was made, 1984)
helium	He	2	4.0	0.95	4.22	(Gk *helios* = sun) Discovered in London as a line in the spectrum of the Sun in 1895 by Janssen (later in the uranium mineral cleveite).
holmium	Ho	67	164.9	1747	2968	(Lat *Holmia* = Stockholm) Discovered in 1879 in Uppsala, Sweden, by P. T. Cleve.
hydrogen	H	1	1.008	14.0	20.3	(Gk *hydro genes* = water forming) Discovered in 1766 in London by Henry Cavendish.
indium	In	49	114.8	429	2353	(= indigo, the colour of its brightest spectral line) Discovered in 1863 in Freiberg, Germany, by F. Reich and T. Richter.
iodine	I	53	126.9	387	458	(Gk *iodes* = violet) Discovered in 1811 in Paris, France, by B. Courtois.
iridium	Ir	77	192.2	2683	4403	(Lat *iris* = rainbow) Discovered in 1803 in London by Smithson Tennant.
iron	Fe	26	55.8	1808	3023	(Anglo-Saxon 'iren') Known to ancient civilisations.

(* = radioactive)

Name	Symbol	Atomic number Z	Relative atomic mass A_r	Melting point/K	Boiling point/K	History and derivation of name
krypton	Kr	36	83.8	117	121	(Gk *kryptos* = hidden) Discovered in 1898 in London by Sir William Ramsey and M. W. Travers.
lanthanum	La	57	138.9	1194	3730	(Gk *lanthanein* = to lie hidden) Discovered in 1839 in Stockholm, Sweden, by C. G. Mosander.
lawrencium	Lr	103	260*	n/a	n/a	(= Ernest Lawrence) Discovered in 1961 in California, USA, by A. Ghiorso and co-workers.
lead	Pb	82	207.2	601	2013	(Anglo-Saxon 'laedan') Known to ancient civilisations – mentioned in Exodus.
lithium	Li	3	6.94	454	1600	(Gk *lithos* = stone) Discovered in 1817 in Stockholm, Sweden, by J. A. Arfvedson (and independently by W. Brande and H. Davy).
lutetium	Lu	71	175.0	1929	3668	(Lat *Lutetia* = Paris) Discovered in 1907 in Paris, France, by G. Urbain and in New Hampshire, USA, by C. James.
magnesium	Mg	12	24.3	922	1363	(Gk *Magnesia* = the district of Thessaly, Greece, where it was first found) First isolated in 1808 in London by Sir Humphrey Davy, though recognised as an element in 1755 in Edinburgh by Joseph Black.
manganese	Mn	25	54.9	1517	2235	(Lat *magnes* = magnet) Isolated in 1774 in Stockholm, Sweden, by J. G. Grahn.
meitnerium	Mt	109	n/a*	n/a	n/a	(= Lisa Meitner) Made 1982.
mendelevium	Md	101	n/a*	n/a	n/a	(= Dmitri Mendeleev) Discovered in 1955 in California, USA, by A. Ghiorso and co-workers.
mercury	Hg	80	200.6	234.3	630	(Lat *Mercurius*, messenger of the gods) Known to ancient civilisations, such as Chinese, Hindu and (1500 BC) Egyptian.
molybdenum	Mo	42	95.9	2890	4885	(Gk *molybdos* = lead) Discovered in 1781 in Uppsala, Sweden, by P. J. Hjelm.
neodymium	Nd	60	144.2	1294	3341	(Gk *neos didymos* = new twin) Discovered in the rare earth didymia in 1885 in Vienna, Austria, by Baron Auer von Welsbach. (See praseodymium)
neon	Ne	10	20.2	24.5	27.1	(Gk *neos* = new) Discovered in 1898 in London by Sir William Ramsey and M. W. Travers.
neptunium	Np	93	237.0*	913	4175	(= the planet Neptune) Discovered in 1940 in California, USA, by E. M. McMillan and P. Abelson.
nickel	Ni	28	58.7	1726	3005	(Ger *kupfernickel* = Devil's – i.e. St Nicholas' or Old Nick's – copper) Discovered in 1751 in Stockholm, Sweden, by A. F. Cronstedt.

(* = radioactive)

Name	Symbol	Atomic number Z	Relative atomic mass A_r	Melting point/K	Boiling point/K	History and derivation of name
niobium	Nb	41	92.9	2741	5015	(Ger myth *Niobe* = daughter of Tantalus) Discovered in 1801 in London by C. Hatchett from ore sent to UK in 17th century by J. Winthrop, Governor of Connecticut, USA. Hence former alternative name of Columbium (= Christopher Columbus) in the USA.
nitrogen	N	7	14.0	63.3	77.4	(Gk *nitron genes* = nitre forming) Discovered in 1776 in Edinburgh by Daniel Rutherford.
nobelium	No	102	259*	n/a	n/a	(= Alfred Nobel) Identified in 1958 in California, USA, by A. Ghiorso and co-workers.
osmium	Os	76	190.2	3327	5300	(Gk *osme* = smell) Discovered in 1803 in London by Smithson Tennant.
oxygen	O	8	16.0	54.8	90.2	(Gk *oxy genes* = acid-forming) Discovered in 1774 in Leeds, England, by Joseph Priestley and in Uppsala, Sweden, by C. W. Scheele.
palladium	Pd	46	106.4	1825	3413	(= the asteroid Pallas, also discovered in 1803) Discovered in 1803 in London by W. H. Wollaston.
phosphorus	P	15	31.0	allotropic: white 317 red 863	553	(Gk *phosphoros* = bringer of light) Discovered in 1669 in Hamburg, Germany, by Hennig Brandt.
platinum	Pt	78	195.1	2045	4100	(Sp *platina* = silver) Known in South America before the arrival of Columbus.
plutonium	Pu	94	244*	914	3505	(= the planet Pluto) Discovered in 1940 in California, USA, by G. T. Seaborg and co-workers.
polonium	Po	84	209*	527	1235	(= Poland) Discovered in pitchblende in 1898 in Paris, France, by Marie Curie.
potassium	K	19	39.1	337	1047	(from Eng potash) Isolated by electrolysis of potash (KOH) in 1807 in London by Sir Humphrey Davy.
praseodymium	Pr	59	140.9	1204	3785	(Gk *prasios dydymos* = green twin) Discovered in the rare earth didymia in 1885 in Vienna, Austria, by Baron Auer von Welsbach. (see neodymium)
promethium	Pm	61	145*	1441	ca. 3000	(Gk myth *Prometheus*) Produced by the irradiation of neodymium in 1947 in Oak Ridge, USA, by J. A. Marinsky and co-workers.
protactinium	Pa	91	231*	2113	4300	(Gk *protos aktino* = first ray) Discovered in 1913 in Berlin, Germany, by Otto Hahn and Lisa Meitner, in Karlsruhe, Germany, by K. Fajans and O. H. Gohring and in Glasgow, Scotland, by Fleck.
radium	Ra	88	226.0*	973	1413	(Lat *radius* = ray) Discovered in pitchblende in 1898 in Paris, France, by Pierre and Marie Curie and isolated in 1911 by Marie Curie and A. Debierne.

(* = radioactive)

Name	Symbol	Atomic number Z	Relative atomic mass A_r	Melting point/K	Boiling point/K	History and derivation of name
radon	Rn	86	222*	202	211	(named after radium) Discovered in decay products of radium in 1900 in Halle, Germany, by F. E. Dorn. Isolated in 1908 in London by Ramsay and Gray. Named radon in 1923.
rhenium	Re	75	186.2	3453	5900	(Lat *Rhenus* = Rhine) Discovered in 1925 in Berlin, Germany, by W. Noddack and co-workers.
rhodium	Rh	45	102.9	2239	4000	(Gk *rhodon* = rose) Discovered in 1803 in London by W. H. Wollaston.
rubidium	Rb	37	65.5	312	961	(Lat *rubidus* = red) Discovered by spectroscopic examination of the mineral lepidolite in 1861 in Heidelberg, Germany, by R. W. Bunsen and G. Kirchoff.
ruthenium	Ru	44	101.1	2583	4173	(Lat *Ruthenia* = Russia) The element first isolated in 1808 in Vilno, Poland by J. A. Sniadecki (and independently by K. K. Klaus).
rutherfordium	Rf	104	?	n/a	n/a	(= Ernest Rutherford) Discovered in 1964 in Dubna, Russia, and in 1969 in California, USA. US claim upheld 1997.
samarium	Sm	62	150.4	1350	2064	(from mineral samarskite) Discovered in 1879 in Paris, France, by P. E. Lecoq de Boisbaudran.
scandium	Sc	21	45.0	1814	3104	(Lat *Scandia* = Scandinavia) Discovered in 1879 in Uppsala, Sweden, by L. F. Nilson. (Properties predicted by D. Mendeleev, who called it ekaboron.)
seaborgium	Sg	106	n/a*	n/a	n/a	(= Glenn T. Seaborg) Made in 1974 at Dubna, Russia, and Berkeley, USA. US claim upheld 1997.
selenium	Se	34	79.0	490	958	(Gk *selene* = moon) Discovered in 1817 in Stockholm Sweden, by J. J. Berzelius.
silicon	Si	14	28.1	1683	2628	(Lat *silicis* = flint) Discovered in 1823 in Stockholm, Sweden, by J. J. Berzelius.
silver	Ag	47	107.9	1235	2485	(Anglo-Saxon *seolfur*) Known to ancient civilisations from at least 3000 BC.
sodium	Na	11	23.0	371.0	1156	(from Eng soda) Isolated by electrolysis of caustic soda (NaOH) in 1807 in London by Sir Humphrey Davy.
strontium	Sr	38	87.6	1042	1657	(ore first found at Strontian, Scotland) Discovered in 1790 in Edinburgh by Sir Humphrey Davy.
sulfur	S	16	32.1	rhombic 386.0 monoclinic 392	718	(Sanscrit *sulvere*, or Lat *sulphurium*, = sulphur) Known to ancient civilisations, and referred to in Genesis as brimstone.
tantalum	Ta	73	181.0	3269	5698	(Gk myth *Tantalus* father of Niobe) Discovered in 1802 in Uppsala, Sweden, by A. G. Ekenberg, but thought to be identical to niobium until 1844.

(* = radioactive)

Name	Symbol	Atomic number Z	Relative atomic mass A_r	Melting point/K	Boiling point/K	History and derivation of name
technetium	Tc	43	98.9*	2445	5150	(Gk *tekhnetos* = artificial) Discovered as a product of the deuteron bombardment of molybdenum in 1937 in Palermo, Italy, by C. Perrier and E. G. Segre.
tellurium	Te	52	127.6	723	1263	(Lat *tellus* = Earth) Discovered in 1782 in Sibiu, Romania, by Baron Muller von Reichenstein.
terbium	Tb	65	158.9	1629	3396	(Swedish town Ytterby = source of mineral) Discovered in 1843 in Stockholm, Sweden, by C. G. Mosander.
thallium	Tl	81	204.4	577	173	(Gk *thallos* = green shoot) Discovered spectroscopically in 1861 in London by W. Crookes.
thorium	Th	90	232.0*	2023	5060	(= Thor, Scandinavian god of war) Discovered in 1828 in Stockholm, Sweden, by J. J. Berzelius.
thulium	Tm	69	168.9	1818	2220	(= Thule, ancient name for Scandinavia) Discovered in 1879 in Uppsala, Sweden, by P. T. Cleve.
tin	Sn	50	118.7	505	2543	(Anglo-Saxon tin) Known to ancient civilisations.
titanium	Ti	22	47.9	1933	3560	(Gk myth the Titans, sons of Uranus and Gaia) Discovered in 1791 in Creed, Cornwall, England, by the Rev. W. Gregor. Not obtained pure until 1910.
tungsten	W	74	183.9	3680	5930	(Swedish *tung sten* = heavy stone) Discovered in 1783 in Vergara, Spain, by J. J. and F. Elhuijar.
uranium	U	92	238.0*	1406	4018	(= the planet Uranus) Discovered in 1789 in Berlin, Germany, by M. H. Klaproth.
vanadium	V	23	50.9	1973	3650	(Old Norse *Vanadis* = goddess Freyja) Discovered in 1801 in Mexico City, Mexico, by A. M. del Rio.
xenon	Xe	54	131.3	61.3	166	(Gk *xenos* = strange) Discovered in 1898 in London by Sir William Ramsay and M. W. Travers.
ytterbium	Yb	70	173.0	1097	1466	(Swedish town Ytterby = source of mineral) Discovered in 1878 in Geneva, Switzerland, by J. C. G. de Marignac.
yttrium	Y	39	88.9	1780	3611	(Swedish village Ytterby = source of mineral) Discovered in 1794 in Abo, Finland, by J. Gadolin.
zinc	Zn	30	65.4	693	1180	(Ger *zink*) Known in India and China before 1500 AD but in brass (Cu/Zn alloy), known to Greeks and Romans before 20 BC.
zirconium	Zr	40	91.2	2125	4650	(Arabic *zargun* = gold colour) Discovered in 1789 in Berlin, Germany, by M. H. Klaproth. Isolated in 1824 in Stockholm, Sweden, by J. J. Berzelius.

(* = radioactive)

3.2F.3 Selected data for some isotopes

Name	Symbol	Mass number	Abundance /percentage	Half-life (y = year)	Mode of decay
hydrogen	H	1	99.985	–	
	H	2	0.015	–	
	H	3	negligible	12.3 y	β^-
carbon	C	12	98.9	–	
	C	13	1.10	–	
	C	14	negligible	5730 y	β^-
oxygen	O	16	99.76	–	
	O	17	0.038	–	
	O	18	0.200	–	
neon	Ne	20	90.5	–	
	Ne	21	0.21	–	
	Ne	22	9.22	–	
sodium	Na	23	100	–	
	Na	24	negligible	14.97 h	β^-
phosphorus	P	31	100	–	
	P	32	negligible	14.3 d	β^-
	P	33	negligible	25.3 d	β^-
chlorine	Cl	35	75.8	–	
	Cl	37	24.2	–	
potassium	K	39	93.3	–	
	K	40	0.0117	1.25×10^9 y	β^-
	K	41	6.73	–	
cobalt	Co	59	100	–	
	Co	60	negligible	5.272 y	β^-
zinc	Zn	64	48.6	–	
	Zn	65	negligible	244 d	β^-
	Zn	66	27.9	–	
	Zn	67	4.1	–	
	Zn	68	18.8	–	
	Zn	70	0.6	–	
bromine	Br	79	50.7	–	
	Br	81	49.3	–	
rubidium	Rb	85	72.2	–	
	Rb	87	27.8	4.9×10^{10} y	β^-
strontium	Sr	84	0.56	–	
	Sr	86	9.86	–	
	Sr	87	7.00	–	
	Sr	88	82.58	–	
	Sr	90	negligible	29 y	β^-
silver	Ag	107	51.8	–	
	Ag	109	48.2	–	
iodine	I	127	100	–	
	I	129	negligible	1.6×10^7 y	β^-
	I	131	negligible	8.04 d	β^-
lead	Pb	204	1.4	–	
	Pb	206	24.1	–	
	Pb	207	22.1	–	
	Pb	208	52.4	–	
	Pb	210	negligible	22.3 y	β^-
radon	Rn	222	negligible	3.82 d	α
radium	Ra	226	negligible	1600 y	α
protactinium	Pa	231	negligible	3.27×10^4 y	α
	Pa	234	negligible	1.17 m	β^-
uranium	U	233	negligible	1.59×10^5 y	α
	U	235	0.72	7.04×10^8 y	α
	U	238	99.28	4.46×10^9 y	α
plutonium	Pu	239	negligible	2.41×10^4 y	α

3.2H   Material properties

3.2H.1   Some common alloys

Alloy	Approximate composition by mass	Useful physical properties
brass	60 Cu, 40 Zn (varies greatly)	golden colour, easily shaped, resistant to corrosion (unless in contact with Al)
bronze	90 Cu, 10 Sn	harder than copper, resistant to corrosion
cast iron	95 Fe, 5 C	expands on freezing, (but brittle)
coinage bronze	75 Cu, 2.5 Sn, 0.5 Zn	hard-wearing
constantan (eureka)	60 Cu, 40 Ni	high electrical resistance and low coefficient of thermal expansion
cupro-nickel	75 Cu, 25 Ni	hard-wearing
duralumin	95 Al, 4 Cu, 1 Mg	low density, resistant to corrosion
solder	30 Sn, 70 Pb (plumbers')	solidifies over a (low) temperature range (520 to 455 K approx.)
	60 Sn, 40 Pb (electronic)	solidifies at one (low) temperature, 455 K approx.
steel	99> Fe, <1 C (variable)	strong, harder the more carbon
stainless steel	73 Fe, 18 Cr, 8 Ni, <1 C	resistant to corrosion, strong

3.2L   Sound

For a discussion of loudness, loudness level and intensity level see Section 8.2L.

The loudness of a sound is a measure of a listener's subjective response and is related to the intensity of the sound. The intensity level of a sound is measured in decibel (dB) against the 'normal' threshold of hearing.

3 dB represents a doubling in intensity.

Permanent loss of hearing results from continuous or habitual exposure to excessively intense noise. Higher frequencies are especially damaging. The effect is cumulative – and not immediately apparent unless the sound is 'explosive'.

3.2L.1   Sound levels

Intensity level/dB	Everyday equivalent
0	threshold of hearing
10	virtual silence, falling leaf
20	quiet room, soft whisper
30	library reading room
40	quiet conversation, birds singing
50	quiet street, normal conversation
60	telephone conversation, inside a busy office
70	inside a large shop, vacuum cleaner 1 m away
75	student refectory
80	loud radio, inside a small car
80–100	recommended maximum levels (depends on frequency)
90	inside a noisy truck, passing train 25 m away
100	food blender 1 m away, howling baby 1 m away
110	amplified rock music
120	road drill
130	threshold of pain, jet aircraft 30 m away

3.2M Biology

3.2M.1 The 20 naturally-occurring amino acids

Those amino acids marked * are essential amino acids required in the human diet. Those marked (*) are required for human growth but can be synthesised by adults.

Trivial name	Code/abbreviation	Discoverer	Date	Formula (all are L-isomers)
alanine	Ala	Weyl	1820	$H_2N-CH-CO_2H$, CH_3
(*) arginine	Arg	Schultze	1886	$H_2N-CH-CO_2H$, CH_2, CH_2, CH_2, NH, C, H_2N NH
asparagine	Asn	Vauquetin	1806	$H_2N-CH-CO_2H$, CH_2, C, O NH_2
aspartic acid	Asp	Ritthausen	1886	$H_2N-CH-CO_2H$, CH_2, CO_2H
cysteine	CysH			$H_2N-CH-CO_2H$, CH_2, SH
glutamic acid	Glu	Ritthausen	1866	$H_2N-CH-CO_2H$, CH_2, CH_2, CO_2H
glutamine	Gln	Schultze	1833	$H_2N-CH-CO_2H$, CH_2, CH_2, C, O NH_2

Trivial name	Code/abbreviation	Discoverer	Date	Formula (all are L-isomers)
glycine	Gly	Braconnet	1820	$H_2N—CH—CO_2H$ | H
(*) histidine	His	Kossel	1896	$H_2N—CH—CO_2H$ | CH_2 | C=CH HN N C
* isoleucine	Ileu	Ehrlich	1903	$H_2N—CH—CO_2H$ | $H—C—CH_3$ | C_2H_5
* leucine	Leu	Proust	1819	$H_2N—CH—CO_2H$ | CH_2 | CH CH_3 CH_3
* lysine	Lys	Drechsel	1889	$H_2N—CH—CO_2H$ | CH_2 | CH_2 | CH_2 | CH_2 | NH_2
* methionine	Met	Mueller	1921	$H_2N—CH—CO_2H$ | CH_2 | CH_2 | S | CH_3
* phenylalanine	Phe	Schultze	1879	$H_2N—CH—CO_2H$ | CH_2 | (phenyl ring)

Trivial name	Code/abbreviation	Discoverer	Date	Formula (all are L-isomers)
proline	Pro	Fischer	1901	$HN-CH-CO_2H$ $H_2C \quad CH_2$ CH_2
serine	Ser	Cramer	1856	$H_2N-CH-CO_2H$ CH_2 OH
* threonine	Thr	Rose	1935	$H_2N-CH-CO_2H$ C $H_3C \quad OH$
* tryptophan	Try	Hopkins	1901	$H_2N-CH-CO_2H$ CH_2 C $HC \quad NH$
tyrosine	Tyr	Liebig	1846	$H_2N-CH-CO_2H$ CH_2 OH
* valine	Val	Gorup-Besanez	1820	$H_2N-CH-CO_2H$ CH $CH_3 \quad CH_3$

3.2M.2 Types of enzyme

International classification of enzymes

Class of enzyme	Types of reaction catalysed
1 oxidoreductases	these enzymes catalyse oxidation-reduction reactions, that is, they transfer hydrogen atoms or electrons from their substrates to acceptor molecules.
2 transferases	small groups of atoms are transferred from one substrate to another.
3 hydrolases	these enzymes split chemical bonds by hydrolysis. Different types attack peptide bonds, glycoside linkages and ester linkages.
4 lyases	these enzymes add new groups to a substrate by breaking a double bond. Alternatively, they may catalyse the formation of double bonds.
5 isomerases	these catalyse internal rearrangement of the atoms in a substrate, that is, they convert between one isomer and another.
6 ligases	new chemical bonds are formed by these enzymes; energy from ATP is needed to make the new bonds. Ligases help in the synthesis of carbohydrates, proteins and other macromolecules.

3.2M.3 Carbohydrates

Classification and major properties of carbohydrates

Group	Properties	Examples
monosaccharides general formula $(CH_2O)_n$, where $n = 3$ to 9	small molecules of low molar mass, sweet-tasting, crystalline, readily soluble in water	trioses, e.g. dihydroxypropanal (glyceraldehyde), $C_3H_6O_3$; pentoses, e.g. ribose, $C_5H_{10}O_5$; hexoses, e.g. glucose, fructose, $C_6H_{12}O_6$
disaccharides general formula $[2(CH_2O)_n - H_2O]$	small molecules with low molar mass, sweet-tasting, crystalline, soluble in water but less so than monosaccharides	sucrose, maltose, lactose; isomers of $C_{12}H_{22}O_{11}$
polysaccharides general formula $(C_5H_{10}O_5)_n$, where $n > 300$	large molecules of high molar mass; do not taste sweet, not crystalline; insoluble or not very soluble in water	glycogen, starch, cellulose

Some commonly-occurring disaccharides

Disaccharide	Constituent monosaccharides	Type of glycosidic bond	Occurrence and importance
lactose	glucose, galactose	1, 4	present in mammalian milk, so important in the diet of infants
maltose	glucose	1, 4	formed by action of enzyme (amylase) on starch during digestion in animals and during germination of seeds
sucrose	glucose, fructose	1, 2	found in sugar cane and sugar beet; form in which sugars are transported in plants, storage compound in some plants such as onions

Summary of features of some common polysaccharides

Polysaccharide	Monomer	Type of glycosidic bond	Shape of molecule
starch	α-glucose (amylose)	1, 4	unbranched chain wound into a helix
starch	α-glucose (amylopectin)	1, 4 with some 1, 6	tightly packed branched chain
glycogen	α-glucose	1, 4 with more 1, 6 than amylopectin	very branched compact molecule
cellulose	β-glucose	1, 4	unbranched straight chains

3.2M.4 The five-kingdom system of classification

Plantae

Photosynthesis
Multicellular and with tissue
   differentiation
Tracheophyta *(vascular plants)*
Bryophyta *(mosses and
   liverworts)*

Fungi

Absorptive nutrition
Multinucleate and mycelial with
   little or no tissue differentiation
Zygomycota *(includes moulds)*
Basidomycota *(includes
   mushrooms)*
Ascomycota *(includes yeasts)*
Deuteromycota *(not a natural
   group; it includes all fungi for
   which sexual reproductive
   structures are not known)*

Animalia

Ingestive or phagotrophic
   nutrition
Multicellular and with tissue
   differentiation
Many phyla

Chlorophyta *(green algae)*
Phaeophyta *(brown algae)*
Rhodophyta *(red algae)*

Myxomycota
(slime moulds)

Protoctista

Eukaryotic organisms not included in other groups

Monera

Protokaryotic organisms
Bacteria and cyanobacteria

3.2M.5 Taxa used in the classification of organisms

Taxon	Description	Human example
kingdom	largest group of organisms sharing common features	Animalia
phylum	major subdivision of a kingdom	Chordata
class	subdivision of a phylum – a group of related orders	Mammalia
order	subdivision of a class – a group of related families	Primates
family	subdivision of an order – a group of related genera	Hominidae
genus	subdivision of a family – a group of related species	*Homo*
species	a group of organisms capable of interbreeding and producing fertile offspring	*H. sapiens*

3.2N   Earth science

3.2N.1   Planetary and solar data

Planet	Diameter /1000 km	Relative mass (Earth = 1)	Density /kg m^{-3}	Mean distance from Sun /million km	Relative equatorial gravity (Earth = 1)	Rotation period (Earth days/hours)	Time to orbit Sun (Earth years/days)	Moons or satellites
Mercury	4.9	0.06	5.43	58	0.3	59 d	88 d	0
Venus	12.1	0.82	5.24	108	0.9	243 d	225 d	0
Earth	12.76	1	5.52	149.6	1	23 h 56 m	365.256 d	1
Moon	*3.5*	*0.012*	*1.9*	*–*	*0.17*	*27.3 d*	*(27.3 d round Earth)*	*n/a*
Mars	6.8	0.11	3.93	228	0.4	25 h	687 d	2
Jupiter	142.8	318	1.32	778	2.3	10 h	12 y	16
Saturn	120	95	0.70	1430	0.9	10 h	29 y	17
Uranus	51.8	14.5	1.25	2870	0.8	17 h	84 y	15
Neptune	49.5	17.1	1.77	4500	1.1	16 h	165 y	8
Pluto	2.3	0.0022	2.00	5900	0.04	6 d	249 y	1
Sun	1392.5	335000	1.41	n/a		25.4 d	n/a	n/a

Note: Earth's mass is 5.975×10^{18} tonne and equatorial gravity is 9.78 m s^{-2}.

3.2N.2   Earth data

Characteristic	Measurement
Earth's radius at the equator	6378 km
Earth's radius from pole to pole	6357 km
Earth's mean radius	6371 km
Earth's circumference at the equator	40 076 km
surface area of oceans	70.8%; 361×10^6 km^2
surface area of land	29.2%; 149×10^6 km^2
mean height of land	840 m
highest point on land – Mount Everest	8846 m
deepest point in ocean – Nero Deep, Marianas Trench	11 035 m
mean depth of ocean	3808 m

3.2N.3   The composition of the Earth's atmosphere

Gases		% by volume in dry air
nitrogen	N_2	78.08
oxygen	O_2	20.94
argon	Ar	0.93
neon	Ne	0.0018
helium	He	0.000 52
methane	CH_4	0.000 17
krypton	Kr	0.000 114
hydrogen	H_2	0.000 05
dinitrogen monoxide	N_2O	0.000 03
xenon	Xe	0.000 0086
Total		99.952 693

Variable component gases		% by volume in dry air
water	H_2O	variable (0–0.7)
ozone	O_3	variable around 0.000 004 (increases with height)
carbon dioxide	CO_2	variable around 0.03

3.2N.4   The structure of the Earth's atmosphere

Height /km	Boundary	Zone	Approximate temperature/°C	Atmospheric pressure /mb*
		thermosphere	increasing upward, to more than 1000 °C	negligible
80	mesopause		38	negligible
		mesosphere	decreasing upward	decreasing upward
56	stratopause		80	1
		stratosphere	steady, then increasing upward	decreasing upward
8–16	tropopause		56	200
		troposphere	decreasing upward	decreasing upward
0	Earth's surface		10	1000

* Pressure is measured in millibars or thousandths of a bar – one bar being 100 kPa or about the atmospheric pressure at the Earth's surface.

3.2N.5 The composition of the Earth's oceans

Constituent	% by mass
water (H$_2$O)	96.5
dissolved constituents	3.5
total	100.0

Dissolved constituents	% by mass of ocean water	% by mass of dissolved constituents	Concentration /mol dm^{-3}
chloride ions (Cl$^-$)	1.93	55.05	0.535
sodium ions (Na$^+$)	1.07	30.61	0.457
sulfate ions (SO$_4^{2-}$)	0.26	7.68	0.028
magnesium ions (Mg^{2+})	0.13	3.69	0.056
calcium ions (Ca^{2+})	0.04	1.16	0.010
potassium ions (K$^+$)	0.04	1.10	0.0097
hydrogencarbonate (HCO$_3^-$)	0.01	0.41	0.0023
bromide (Br$^-$) boric acid (H$_3$BO$_3$) strontium (Sr^{2+}) fluorine (F$^-$)	0.01 total	0.29	0.0014
total	3.49	99.99	1.0994

Note: The salinity (% dissolved constituents by mass) of the open ocean is 3.5%, as shown above. The Mediterranean Sea has a salinity of 3.9%, the northern end of the Red Sea is 4.1% and the Dead Sea has a salinity of 27%.

3.2N.6 The composition of the Earth's crust

Element	% by mass
oxygen	46.60
silicon	27.72
aluminium	8.13
iron	5.00
calcium	3.63
sodium	2.83
potassium	2.59
magnesium	2.09
titanium	0.44
hydrogen	0.14
phosphorus	0.12
all other elements	0.71
total	100.00

3.2N.7 The composition of the whole Earth

Element	% by mass
iron	35.0
oxygen	30.0
silicon	15.0
magnesium	13.0
nickel	2.4
sulfur	1.9
calcium	1.1
aluminium	1.1
all other elements	0.5
total	100.00

Note: These figures are estimates – direct measurements are not possible!

3.2N.8 The structure of the Earth

Zone	Boundary name	Depth below surface /km	Velocity of P waves /km s⁻¹	Velocity of S waves /km s⁻¹	State	Density /kg m⁻³	Composition	Pressure in units of 10^6 bar
	sea level	0						10^{-6}
Crust (continental)			6–8	3–4	solid	2.7–2.9	granitic	
	Moho (Mohorovicic discontinuity)	33						9000
Upper mantle			7.9–8.1	4.6–4.8	solid	3.32 and increasing	peridotitic (olivine and pyroxene)	
		50						
Upper mantle – low velocity zone			7.8	4.3	solid with 1 to 10% liquid	increasing	olivine and pyroxene	
		250						
Upper mantle			8.1–8.9	4.6–5.1	solid	increasing to 3.54	olivine and pyroxene	
	transition zone	400						
Upper mantle			9.1–10.3	5.3–5.6	solid	3.72–3.99	spinel and pyroxene	
	transition zone	670						382 000
Lower mantle			10.8–13.7	6.0–7.2	solid	4.38–5.57	perovskite and magnesium oxide	
	core/mantle boundary	2891						1368 000
Outer core			8.1–10.4	0	liquid	9.90–12.2	mainly iron, possibly some nickel, silicon, sulfur or oxygen	
	outer core/ inner core boundary	5149						c.3 300 000
Inner core			11.0	3.6	solid	12.8–13.1	mainly iron, possibly some nickel, silicon, sulfur or oxygen	
	centre of the Earth	6371						c.3 600 000

Note: 1 The Moho has an average depth of 30 km below the surface of the crust which conceals an extensive range. Below the oceanic crust it can be as shallow as 5 km; below the thickened continental crust of mountain ranges such as the Himalayas the depth can be approximately 70 km.

2 The solid **lithosphere** comprises the crust and the upper part of the mantle; it is broken into plates. Its thickness varies from 1–2 km beneath constructive margins (where the plates are moving apart and new plate material is being formed) to 300 km beneath continental collision zones, with a mean thickness of around 100 km. Beneath the solid lithosphere is the **asthenosphere** (solid with 1–10% liquid) which is ductile and can flow over geological time; it includes the low velocity zone.

3 The crust and mantle are distinguished on the basis of chemical differences, while the lithosphere and asthenosphere are distinguished on mechanical differences.

3.2N.9   The 'modified Mercalli' intensity scale for earthquakes

Intensity	Designation	Description of characteristic effects
I	instrumental	detected only by seismographs
II	feeble	noticed only by sensitive people at rest, particularly on upper floors
III	slight	like the vibrations due to a passing lorry; may not be recognised as an earthquake
IV	moderate	felt by people when walking; rocking of loose objects, swinging of hanging objects
V	rather strong	felt generally, most sleepers are wakened and bells ring; liquids may spill, small objects may fall
VI	strong	trees sway and all suspended objects swing; damage by falling loose objects; many people run out of doors; weak walls crack
VII	very strong	general alarm; difficulty with walking; walls crack , plaster and loose bricks and tiles fall
VIII	destructive	car drivers seriously disturbed; walls cracked, chimneys fall; poorly constructed buildings damaged
IX	ruinous	general panic; some houses collapse, others badly damaged; ground begins to crack; underground pipes break
X	disastrous	ground cracks badly; many buildings destroyed; dams damaged; railway lines bent; landslides on steep slopes
XI	very disastrous	few buildings remain standing; bridges destroyed; all services (railways, pipes and cables) out of action; great landslides and floods
XII	catastrophe	total destruction; objects thrown into the air; ground rises and falls in waves

Note: The Mercalli intensity scale is a measure of the damage caused by the earthquake at different distances from the earthquake epicentre. Many Mercalli intensity observations can be used to plot isoseismal lines – lines of equal earthquake intensity.

3.2N.10   The Richter scale of earthquake magnitude

Magnitude	Characteristic effects	Amount of slip on faults/m	Energy released /J	Number of earth-quakes per year
3	not felt but recorded	0.008	2×10^9	100 000
4	felt by many	0.025	6×10^{10}	15 000
5	felt by all	0.08	2×10^{12}	3000
6	slight damage to buildings	0.25	6×10^{13}	100
7	serious damage; rails bent	0.8	2×10^{15}	20
8	damage nearly total	2.5	6×10^{16}	2
9	catastrophic	8	2×10^{18}	very uncommon

Note: The Richter scale is a measure of the magnitude of the earthquake at the epicentre. It is a logarithmic scale, with an increase in magnitude of 1 meaning an earthquake of 10 times the size. The greatest earthquake magnitude yet recorded is around 9.5 on the Richter scale.

3.2N.11 The characteristics of seismic waves

Seismic wave	Other names	Mode of propagation	Properties	Formula for calculating velocity	Energy dispersal
surface waves	the two types of surface waves are Love (L) and Rayleigh waves	movement of the surface of the Earth	reduce in intensity more quickly than other waves; these 'ground-moving' waves cause the devastation of earthquakes		$1/d$
primary waves (body waves)	P- push; pressure; compression; longitudinal	compression and rarefaction of particles within the Earth	faster of the two types of body waves; travel through solids and liquids but more slowly through liquids; oscillatory particle motion is in wave travel direction	$v = \sqrt{\dfrac{K + \frac{4}{3}\mu}{\rho}}$	$1/d^2$
secondary waves (body waves)	S- shear; transverse	movement of particles by shear, or motion at right angles to the wave-travel direction	slower of the two types of body waves; not transmitted by liquids (or other fluids)	$v = \sqrt{\dfrac{\mu}{\rho}}$	$1/d^2$

Note: In the formulae, K is the bulk modulus (a measure of the compressibility of the material); μ is the shear modulus (a measure of the rigidity of the material); ρ is the density of the material; d is the distance travelled.

3.2N.12 Major economic minerals and rocks

Minerals

Mineral name	Chemical formula	Major occurrences	Property(ies) used	Some major uses
barite (barytes)	$BaSO_4$	gangue mineral in hydrothermal veins	relatively high density (RD 4.5)	to increase density of oil-well drilling muds; to increase weight of high-quality writing paper
bauxite	$Al_2O_3.2H_2O$	product of weathering under tropical conditions	aluminium content	main ore of aluminium
cassiterite	SnO_2	hydrothermal veins and placer deposits	tin content	main ore of tin
chalcopyrite	$CuFeS_2$	hydrothermal veins	copper content	main ore of copper
diamond	C	'pipes' of volcanic rock called kimberlite and placer deposits	hardness (10 on Mohs' scale); gem qualities (adamantine lustre, hardness, rarity)	industrial cutting and abrasive tools; gemstones
fluorite (fluorspar)	CaF_2	gangue mineral in hydrothermal veins	fluorine content	main source of fluorine (aerosol propellants, refrigeration, tooth care)
galena	PbS	hydrothermal veins	lead content	main ore of lead
graphite	C	metamorphism of carbon-rich rocks	'softness' (hardness on Mohs' scale 1–2); electrical conductivity; heat resistance	lubricant and pencil 'leads' (due to 'softness'); in carbon electrodes; in heat resistant materials
gold (native gold)	Au	hydrothermal veins, but mainly in placer deposits	rarity of gold; lack of chemical reactivity	currency; jewellery
gypsum	$CaSO_4.2H_2O$	deposited by evaporating sea water	converted to plaster of Paris ($CaSO_4.\frac{1}{2}H_2O$) by heating	plaster is used for plastering walls and broken limbs

(continued)

Mineral name	Chemical formula	Major occurrences	Property(ies) used	Some major uses
haematite	Fe_2O_3	pre-Cambrian sedimentary deposits; vein deposits	iron content	a major ore of iron
halite	NaCl	deposited by evaporating sea water	sodium and chlorine content; salt taste; food preservative; depresses freezing point of water	source of sodium compounds (carbonate and hydroxide); source of chlorine (for bleach and hydrochloric acid); food seasoning and preserving; salting icy roads
magnetite	Fe_3O_4	magmatic segregation	iron content	a major ore of iron
muscovite mica	$KAl_2(AlSi_3)O_{10}(OH)_2$	large crystals in very large coarse igneous dykes called pegmatites	insulating properties	insulation in electrical apparatus
quartz	SiO_2	a wide variety of rocks; pure in vein quartz; fairly pure in quartz-rich sands and metaquartzites	transparent when fused (melted and suddenly solidified); hardness (7 on Mohs' scale); silicon content; piezoelectric effect	glass-making; abrasive; source of silicon compounds; source of industrial quartz used in electrical apparatus (silicon chips)
sphalerite	ZnS	hydrothermal mineral	zinc content	major ore of zinc
talc	$Mg_6Si_4O_{10}(OH)_2$	alteration of magnesium-bearing rocks	'softness' (1 on Mohs' scale); lack of reactivity	talcum powder; filler in paints, paper, rubber, etc.

Rocks

Rock name	Composition	Major occurrence	Property(ies) used	Major uses
brick clay	clay minerals and fine quartz grains	fine mud deposited in quiet conditions	can be moulded; becomes very hard when fired (heated in kiln)	bricks, tiles, coarse earthenware
china clay	kaolin	hydrothermal alteration of feldspars in granite	can be moulded; becomes very hard when fired; lack of reactivity	high quality pottery; filler in paints, paper, rubber, textiles, etc.
facing and ornamental stones	igneous, sedimentary and metamorphic rocks	wide variety, including coarse-grained igneous rocks (granite, gabbro, etc.), limestones, sandstones, marbles, slates	resistance to weathering; can be cut into slabs; attractive	thin slabs as facing stones on prestigious buildings; gravestones, fireplaces, etc.
limestone (including chalk)	calcium carbonate $CaCO_3$, mostly calcite	sedimentary deposits, largely under shallow tropical sea conditions	forms cement when heated with other materials; source of calcium oxide; homogeneous rock	cement manufacture; calcium oxide has wide uses in the chemical industry; neutralises acidic soils; aggregate for concrete and foundations; used in iron smelting, glass manufacture
sand and gravel	sedimentary deposits	deposited largely by rivers and on beaches	bulk out cement and concrete	construction industry

Notes: **1** Hydrothermal veins were deposited by rising hot solutions in rock fractures.

2 Gangue minerals are the normally non-economic minerals associated in mineral veins with ore minerals.

3 Placer deposits are sedimentary concentrations of dense minerals.

4 Magmatic segregation occurs when first formed minerals sink in magma chambers.

3.2N.13 Mohs' scale of hardness

Mineral	Hardness on Mohs' scale	Hardness of other material used in mineral hardness testing	Relative hardness measured by modern methods
talc	1		1
gypsum	2		2
		finger nail – around 2.5	
calcite	3		3
		'copper' coin – around 3.5	
fluorite (fluorspar)	4		4
apatite	5		5
		pocket-knife blade point of a pair of compasses common window glass – around 5.5	
orthoclase feldspar	6		6
		steel file - around 6.5	
quartz	7		7
topaz	8		8
corundum	9		9
diamond	10		40

Notes: 1 The originator of the scale was a man called Mohs, so the apostrophe comes after the 's' in his name.

2 Mohs' scale of hardness applies only to minerals; rock hardness cannot be measured on the scale, since rocks are aggregates of minerals.

3 Mohs devised his scale in 1824 without the advantage of modern technology. However, when his choice of minerals was checked by modern methods, the steps of increasing hardness were almost identical, except for diamond, which is much harder than corundum. Mohs' scale is still in wide use today.

3.2N.14 Rock classification

Rocks are formed by a variety of interacting processes and so are classified using a range of criteria. Initial classification is based on the major mode of formation (i.e. igneous – from molten rock, sedimentary – laid down by surface processes, and metamorphic – altered by heat and/or pressure) – thereafter, different methods of classification are used.

Igneous rocks

	Chemical /mineralogical classification (silicon content of whole rock)			
	Silicic (acid)	Intermediate	Mafic (basic)	Ultramafic (ultrabasic)
silicon content of whole rock, expressed as % of silicon as an oxide	more than 66	66–52	52–45	less than 45
predominant minerals	feldspar and quartz	feldspar and ferromagnesian (dark-coloured) minerals (little or no quartz)	ferromagnesian minerals (little or no quartz)	ferromagnesian minerals (little or no feldspar)
feldspar composition	sodium- and potassium-rich	intermediate	calcium-rich	none

Crystal size classification (mean diameter of largest common grains) Rock name				
glassy, no crystals	volcanic glass (or pumice, if 'frothy')			
fine, less than 1 mm	rhyolite	andesite	basalt	very rare
medium, 1–5 mm	microgranite	microdiorite	dolerite	very rare
coarse, more than 5 mm	granite	diorite	gabbro	peridotite

Note: Ferromagnesian minerals contain iron and/or magnesium which give them a dark colour; the main ones are olivine, pyroxene, amphibole and biotite.

Sedimentary rocks

Sedimentary rock type	Sedimentary rock name	Description
clastic	breccia	coarse-grained rock with angular fragments
clastic	conglomerate	coarse-grained rock with rounded fragments, mean grain size more than 2 mm
clastic	sandstone (or arenite)	medium-grained rock, mean grain size between 2 mm and 1/16 mm (0.0625 mm)
clastic	arkose sandstone	sandstone with more than 25% feldspar, modern terminology: arkosic arenite
clastic	orthoquartzite sandstone	sandstone with more than 95% quartz, modern terminology: quartz arenite
clastic	greywacke sandstone	sandstone with more than 15% mud matrix
clastic	siltstone	fine-grained rock, mean grain size between 1/16 and 1/256 mm (0.0625–0.0039 mm)
clastic	clay	fine-grained rock (even though it is often soft) with mean grain size less than 0.0039 mm
clastic	mudstone	fine-grained rock that is massive (is not well-bedded or layered)
clastic	shale	fine-grained silt and/or clay grade rock that is fissile (splits easily into fragments)
carbonate	limestone	rocks of varying grain size containing more than 50% calcium carbonate – often formed of fossil debris
carbonate	chalk	very fine-grained limestone, usually white in colour – formed of microfossil debris
chemical	rock salt	rock formed of the evaporite mineral halite (sodium chloride)
chemical	ironstone	an iron-rich sedimentary rock
chemical	chert (called flint when found in chalk)	forms nodules and layers that grow when lime-rich sediments become hardened into limestones, formed of fine-grained (cryptocrystalline) silica
organic	coal	carbon-rich sedimentary rock formed from plant remains

Note: Clastic rocks are formed of sediment derived from erosion.

Metamorphic rocks

Metamorphism by high temperatures alone (called thermal metamorphism) produces a different range of metamorphic rocks from that produced by heat and pressure combined (in regional metamorphism).

1 Regional metamorphic rocks

Primary rock type		Low-grade metamorphism		Moderate-grade metamorphism		High-grade metamorphism	
Rock type	*Main minerals*	*Rock name /description*	*Main minerals*	*Rock name /description*	*Main minerals*	*Rock name /description*	*Main minerals*
Shale and mudstone	quartz clay minerals feldspar	Slate (very fine-grained – flat breakage surfaces, several dark colours) Phyllite (fine-grained, undulating surfaces, greenish sheen)	quartz muscovite chlorite feldspar	Schist (medium- to coarse-grained, splits parallel to aligned crystals, variable colours)	quartz muscovite chlorite biotite garnet staurolite kyanite sillimanite hornblende epidote feldspar	Gneiss (coarse-grained – usually banded, bands often have complex folding)	quartz muscovite biotite feldspar garnet hornblende
Basalt	pyroxene feldspar	Greenschist Greenstone (fine-grained, greenish colour)	chlorite feldspar	Amphibolite (medium-grained, splits parallel to aligned crystals, dark coloured)	hornblende feldspar	Amphibolite (medium-grained, splits parallel to aligned crystals, dark coloured)	hornblende feldspar
Limestone	calcite	Medium-grained marble (crystals usually equal-dimensional, various colours)	calcite	Medium- to coarse-grained marble	calcite	Coarse-grained marble (crystals may be bent and twinned, various colours)	calcite
Sandstone (quartz-rich varieties)	quartz	Medium-grained metaquartzite (elongated crystals, pale coloured)	quartz	Medium- to coarse-grained metaquartzite (elongated crystals, pale coloured)	quartz	Coarse-grained metaquartzite (elongated crystals, pale coloured	quartz

2 Thermal (contact) metamorphic rocks

Primary rock type		Low-grade metamorphism		High-grade metamorphism	
Rock name	*Main minerals*	*Rock name/description*	*Main minerals*	*Rock name/description*	*Main minerals*
Shale and mudstone	quartz clay minerals feldspar	Spotted rock (similar to original rock, but with dark spots)	quartz clay minerals feldspar andalusite graphite	Hornfels (massive fine- to medium-grained rock, hard and difficult to break)	quartz andalusite biotite cordierite sillimanite
Limestone	calcite	Medium-grained marble (equal-dimensional crystals, various colours)	calcite	Coarse-grained marble (equal-dimensional crystals, various colours)	calcite
Sandstone (quartz-rich varieties)	quartz	Medium-grained meta-quartzite (equal-dimensional crystals, various colours)	quartz	Coarse-grained meta-quartzite (equal-dimensional crystals, various colours)	quartz

3.2N.15　　The geological time scale

The divisions of geological time and major events since the formation of the Earth

Eon *Duration Ma* **Start, Ma**	Key stages in the evolution of life	Key events	Oxygen content of the atmosphere	Global temperature change
Phanerozoic *545* **545**	*See* Phanerozoic geological column (page 42)	*See* Phanerozoic geological column (page 42) for more details • Frequency of fires in Carb. coal forests indicates oxygen levels similar to or even higher than today • Land animals appear – need oxygen levels about present values	Present day	Ice Ice Ice
Proterozoic *1930* **2500**	• Ediacaran faunas in Australia, Russia, China Soft-bodied animals • Silica skeletons in single-celled algae • Stromatolites decline (grazers) • Stromatolites at their maximum; eukaryote diversification • Multicellular marine organisms evolve – eukaryotes with nucleus and cytoplasm – needing oxygen above 0.1% • Size of cell doubles • Gunflint chert (Canada/US) stromatolite • Single-celled eukaryotes	• Break-up of early supercontinent • Orogeny in Scottish rocks • Soft-bodied metazoan fossils first appear – need oxygen levels above 2% • Glaciation – Scotland, Greenland, Africa, China • Glaciation – Australia, China, S. Africa • Glaciation –Greenland, Scandinavia • Formation of early supercontinent • Orogeny in Scottish rocks • End of major banded ironstone deposition (iron deposited in Fe^{2+} state, indicating low oxygen levels) • First red beds deposited, iron in Fe^{3+} state – must have been significant amount of oxygen in atmosphere	Present day	Major ice age Present day Ice age
Archean *1300* **3800**	 • Stromatolites • Prokaryotes – bacteria and photosynthesising blue-green bacteria (algae)	• Continental cores of most major continents formed by this time • Orogeny in Scottish rocks • Oxygen produced by early life forms • Earliest banded ironstones deposited (iron deposited in Fe^{2+} state, indicating little or no oxygen present) • First sedimentary rocks formed (Greenland) • Greenstone belts in India, Australia, S. Africa, Canada	30% 20% 10% None Cold Warm	
Hadean *800* **4600**	None	• First oceans probably formed • Volcanic outgassing and contributions from asteroids, etc., produced secondary atmosphere • Volcanic activity widespread on cooling Earth. Radioactive decay at higher rate than now • Zircon dates from igneous source rocks in NW Australia • Continuous bombardment by asteroid-like bodies caused Earth to become very hot – probably a few thousand degrees • Formation of Earth and growth through collision of many asteroid-like bodies	None	

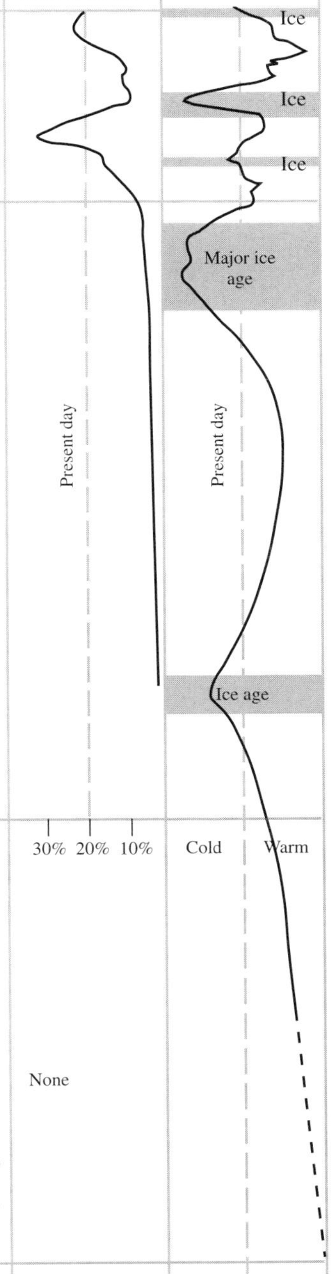

Precambrian (left margin spanning Proterozoic, Archean, Hadean)

The divisions of geological time and major events since 570 million years ago (Phanerozoic time)

Eon	Era	Period *Duration Ma* **Start Ma**	Key stages in the evolution of life and common life forms	The diversity of of life *(variation in number of families)*	Key events	Global sea level change	UK latitude *(approx.)*
Phanerozoic	Cenozoic	**Quaternary** *1.64* **Tertiary** *63* **65**	Early humans Increase in mammals Horses, cows, elephants, pigs, apes, dogs, bears, etc. appear and increase Flowering plants in full development	Increasing Decreasing < >	Major glaciation Linking of N & S America Alpine orogeny in UK; Alps formed as Tethys closed Widespread igneous activity in northern UK Collision of India with Asia Separation of Australia and Antarctica	High Low < >	55° N 40° N
	Mesozoic	**Cretaceous** *77* **142**	Extinction of dinosaurs & ammonites Primates evolve Mammals and flowering plants (angiosperms) appear		Opening of North Atlantic Ocean began		35° N
		Jurassic *64* **206**	Dinosaurs and ammonites abundant Birds and mammals appear			Present day	30° N
		Triassic *42* **248**	Mammals evolve Flying dinosaurs and reptiles appear First modern corals Ammonites evolve		Opening of South Atlantic Ocean began		
	Upper Palaeozoic	**Permian** *42* **290**	Mass extinction Rise of reptiles and winged insects Conifers and beetles appear		Formation of Pangea supercontinent Major glaciation Hercynian/Variscan orogeny in Europe – closing of the Rheic Ocean		10° N
		Carboniferous *64* **354**	Coal forest plants First reptiles and winged insects Seed-bearing plants (gymnosperms)				0° N
		Devonian *63* **417**	First amphibians and ammonoids Earliest trees and spiders Rise of fishes Graptolites become extinct				20° S
	Lower Palaeozoic	**Silurian** *26* **443**	First spore-bearing land plants; first soils Earliest known coral reefs		Climax of Caledonian orogeny – closing of Iapetus, Laurentian plate joined to European plate		
		Ordovician *52* **495**	First fish-like vertebrates Trilobites and graptolites abundant Corals appear		Major glaciation	Present day	30° S
		Cambrian *50* **545**	Trilobites, graptolites, brachiopods, molluscs, crinoids, radiolaria and foraminifera The 'Cambrian explosion' – complex marine organism evolve with $CaCO_3$ shells – abundant fossils first appear	Increasing Decreasing < >			

Note: all geological periods are subdivided into epochs, as:

Period	Epoch	Start/Ma
Quaternary	Holocene or Recent	0.01
	Pleistocene	1.64
Tertiary	Pliocene	5.2
	Miocene	25.5
	Oligocene	35
	Eocene	56.5
	Palaeocene	65

3.2N.16 The ranges of major fossil groups

Major group	Sub-group	Minor group	First appearance	Greatest number of families	Extinction
molluscs	bivalves		early Cambrian	today	not extinct
molluscs	gastropods		late Cambrian	today	not extinct
molluscs	cephalopods	nautiloids ammonoids	mid Cambrian mid Devonian	Ordovician Triassic	not extinct end Cretaceous
brachiopods			early Cambrian	Devonian	not extinct
echinoderms	echinoids		late Ordovician	Tertiary	not extinct
trilobites			early Cambrian	Cambrian	end Permian
graptolites	dendroids		late Cambrian	Ordovician	early Carboniferous
graptolites	graptoloids		early Ordovician	Ordovician	early Devonian
corals	scleractinian		early Triassic	Cretaceous	not extinct
corals	rugose		late Ordovician	Devonian	end Permian
corals	tabulate		early Ordovician	Silurian	end Permian
foraminifera			early Cambrian	today	not extinct
vertebrates	fish		late Cambrian	today	not extinct
vertebrates	amphibians		late Devonian	Permian	not extinct
vertebrates	reptiles		mid Carboniferous	Cretaceous	not extinct
vertebrates	mammals		late Triassic	today	not extinct
land plants	vascular plants		late Silurian	today	not extinct

3.2N.17 The stratigraphic principles

Principle or Law	Explanation
Principle of superposition of strata	Strata laid down on top of other strata are always younger unless the sequence has been changed by unusual circumstances such as major earth movements
Principle of lateral continuity	Strata normally continue laterally for long distances; they stop only by petering out or by meeting the edge of the depositional area
Principle of original horizontality	Strata are normally deposited as horizontal or near-horizontal layers
Law of cross-cutting relationships	Anything that cuts across anything else must be younger; examples include dykes, fractures, faults and unconformities that are younger than the rocks across which they cut
Law of included fragments	Fragments of rocks included in other rocks must be older; examples include pebbles in conglomerates and xenoliths in igneous rocks that are older than the rocks in which they are found
Law of faunal succession	Strata may include assemblages of fossils by which they can be recognised and correlated; the assemblages always occur in the same order (although some may be missing from the sequence)

Notes: 1 Principles normally apply, Laws always apply.

2 Sedimentary rocks are deposited in layers called strata.

3.2N.18 The major weathering processes

Type of weathering	Weathering process	Description	Products	Example(s)
Chemical	Solution	Soluble materials dissolve and are carried away in solution	Solutions	Dissolving of the results of carbonation weathering
	Carbonation	Rainwater containing CO_2 from the air and soil reacts with carbonates to form soluble hydrogencarbonates	Calcium (Ca^{2+}) and hydrogencarbonate (HCO_3^-) ions	Attack on calcite, aragonite and limestone
	Hydrolysis	Water reacts with minerals, particularly silicate minerals like feldspars, breaking them down; if the water contains CO_2, more hydrogen ions (H^+) are available and hydrolysis is speeded up	Water-poor clay minerals and ions in solution	Hydrolysis of feldspar to the clay mineral kaolinite; hydrolysis of olivine to serpentine and iron minerals
	Hydration	The addition of water molecules to the atomic structures of minerals	Water-poor minerals become water-rich minerals	Hydration of anhydrite to gypsum; hydration of water-poor to water-rich clay minerals
	Oxidation	The addition of oxygen to the atomic structures of minerals or a similar chemical change	Minerals gain oxygen and the number of charges on the ion increases	Greenish iron minerals containing Fe^{2+} oxidise to red or brown iron minerals containing Fe^{3+}
	Ion exchange	Minerals rich in one ion are attacked by a solution rich in another ion and the ions exchange, e.g. Na^+ can exchange for Ca^{2+}	Minerals lose ions and gain different ions	Na-rich clay minerals alter to Ca-rich clay minerals
Physical	Insolation	Heating and cooling of rocks in desert regions causes minerals to expand and contract at different rates until the rock eventually fractures	Angular rock fragments	The 'spalling' of granite in arid areas
	Wetting and drying	Minerals absorb water through hydration and expand	Rock weakened by expanding minerals	Clay mineral expansion weakens rock
	Freezing and thawing	Water expands by 9% on freezing, so fractures filled with water are prized further apart each time the water freezes until the fragment breaks off	Angular rock fragments	Screes found below cliff faces in mountain areas that freeze at night
	Crystallisation of minerals	New minerals grow in rock spaces forcing the rock apart	Angular rock fragments	Gypsum crystals growing along fractures in shales
	Stress release	Deeply-buried rocks are compressed by the pressure of the rocks above; when the overburden is removed, the rock expands to produce stress release joints	Near-horizontal jointing	Near-horizontal jointing in granite; the breaking away of curved sheets of granite in exfoliation
Physical/ biological	Plant roots	Plant roots grow in fractures forcing them apart	Fractures are widened	
Chemical /biological	Chelation	Organic compounds from soil remove metal ions from minerals	Minerals lose metal ions and so decay	Minerals in soils decay

(continued)

Type of weathering	Weathering process	Description	Products	Example(s)
Biological	Bacterial action	Many minerals decompose far more quickly in the presence of bacteria		
	Soil processes	Organic activity increases weathering rates dramatically, e.g. providing CO_2 for hydrolysis and carbonation and organic compounds for chelation	Soil formation	

Notes: 1 The different weathering processes interact; rarely is one process alone responsible for weathering.
2 Biological activity is crucial in accelerating many weathering processes.
3 Most physical activity is accelerated by chemical activity.

3.2N.19 The structure of soils

Most soils are formed of three main horizontal layers, called horizons; in detail, these may be subdivided into many more sub-layers.

Soil horizon	Main processes active
Surface of soil	
A horizon	high content of organic material; water passing through this horizon carries soluble materials and clay downwards; this horizon becomes depleted or leached of materials
B horizon	clay and some soluble materials are deposited at this level; this horizon becomes enriched in materials
C horizon	the passage of soil into bedrock takes place here; groundwater flow can carry soluble materials away
Bedrock – solid rock or unaltered material underlying the soil	

3.2N.20 The major processes of erosion

Agent	Process	Result
gravity	falling	material weakened by weathering falls off steep rock faces
	sliding	weakened material slides away (lubrication by water is an important factor). Sliding may be triggered by earthquake activity; less competent beds like clays are more likely to slide than more competent rocks like limestones; slides may turn into slumps, slumps may become debris flows, debris flow may become density currents
water	hydraulic action	loose sediment is removed by flow of water; fragments are broken off by the power of water, particularly in floods or by waves in storms
	abrasion	fragments carried by water grind down the rocks over which they travel
	attrition	fragments themselves get ground down during transport, largely by collision with each other
wind	wind action	loose sediment is removed and transported by the wind; materials are broken off by the wind in storms
	abrasion	rocks become ground down by sand blasting
	attrition	the particles themselves become broken down in sand blasting through particle collision
ice	plucking	solid rock fragments pulled off by ice movement – glacial ice melts, then refreezes around a protruding rock, which is wrenched off when the ice moves
	abrasion	rock material carried at the base of the moving ice grinds down the bedrock below
	attrition	rock material carried at the base of the moving ice becomes ground down

Notes: 1 Much erosion by gravity involves water.
2 All agents are affected by gravity; water and ice flow downhill and wind is a density flow of air influenced by gravity.

3.2N.21   The major diagenetic (sedimentary rock-forming) processes

Diagenetic process	Description	Result	Example
compaction	sediment is squeezed by the pressure of the overlying sediment, removing water as porosity and permeability are reduced	sands contain hard minerals that resist compaction; clay minerals in muds become greatly compacted	compaction has little effect on sands; muds become mudstones
pressure solution	minerals dissolve more readily at points where they are under pressure, so solution occurs where grains press into one another	where pebbles are in contact, pits are produced; quartz grains dissolve when they are in contact; in limestones, irregular solution surfaces called stylolites are produced	material dissolved through pressure solution is then available as cement
solution	flowing pore waters have increased power to dissolve and transport because of the high water pressures	the calcium carbonate mineral aragonite is commonly dissolved; calcite and quartz may also dissolve, depending on conditions	fossils made of aragonite dissolve leaving moulds; solutions rich in dissolved calcium carbonate and/or quartz are produced
recrystallisation	some minerals, particularly calcite, change in size and shape	fine calcite muds become coarse calcite mosaics	lime mud becomes limestone, losing much porosity and permeability
replacement	one mineral becomes changed to another in a progressive, molecule by molecule, change	aragonite changes to its more stable polymorph, calcite; calcium in calcium carbonate minerals becomes replaced by magnesium to become dolomite; nodules of chert grow in fine limestones, like chalk ironstone nodules grow in shales	ancient limestones are composed of calcite; limestones become dolomitised; nodules of chalk are silicified to form flint; irregular chert nodules and layers form in other limestones; rounded nodules form in iron-rich shales
cementation	minerals crystallise in pore spaces from circulating fluids, cementing grains together	quartz commonly cements sands; calcite cements lime sediments; iron mineral cements are common in sandstones and some limestones	sands become hard sandstones; lime sediments become limestones; sands become relatively soft sandstones of various colours while some limestones are buff coloured
authigenic mineral formation	new minerals, such as clay minerals and glauconite, grow within pore spaces from circulating fluids	porosity and permeability are reduced	pore spaces become filled

3.2N.22 The major fossilisation processes

Group of processes	Process	Results	Frequency
preservation with little alteration	freezing	body deep frozen in ice	very unusual
	mummification	body dries out in arid areas	very unusual
	peat-bog preservation	body preserved in anaerobic peat-bog environment	very unusual
	tar-pit preservation	body falls into anaerobic tar pit and becomes sealed in	very unusual
	preservation in amber	body becomes sealed into sticky pine-tree resin that becomes hard amber	very unusual
	burial of calcite ($CaCO_3$) remains in fine-grained sediments	these common hard parts of many invertebrates become preserved as buried	common
	burial of aragonite ($CaCO_3$) remains in fine-grained sediments	most coral and mollusc 'hard parts' are aragonite – become preserved as buried	common, but rare in rocks older than Mesozoic
	burial of calcium phosphate ($Ca_3(PO_4)_2$ remains in fine-grained sediments	brachiopod hard parts and vertebrate bones and teeth become preserved as buried	fairly common
	burial of silica (SiO_2 – in its opaline form) remains in fine-grained sediments	sponge and some protozoan hard parts become preserved as buried	fairly common, but rare in rocks older than Cenozoic
altered in fossilisation	carbonisation of soft parts – carbon films form in anaerobic environments	organic soft parts preserved as carbon films	very unusual
	carbonisation – hard organic skeletons become carbonised	chitin skeletons of arthropods and graptolites become altered to carbon	fairly uncommon
	permineralisation – minerals deposited in pore spaces of skeleton (also called petrifaction)	porous skeletons become solid mineral – commonly $CaCO_3$, less commonly SiO_2, glauconite, iron compounds, etc.	fairly uncommon
	recrystallisation – minerals forming the skeleton alter in shape and size, filling pore spaces	porous skeletons become solid	fairly uncommon
	replacement – one mineral becomes replaced by another, molecule by molecule, or one mineral may replace another en masse	aragonite becomes replaced by its more stable polymorph calcite; other materials become replaced by other minerals, e.g. calcite by iron pyrites; calcite by silica; etc.	very common
preservation as moulds or casts	mould formation – the imprint of a soft-bodied organism or of hard parts remains in the rock	depressions are left by soft parts or when hard parts, like shells, are dissolved away; moulds of outsides of shells are external moulds, of insides of shells are internal moulds	common
	cast formation – a mould is filled by sediment or a mineral and this is preserved when the mould is is removed	casts tend to stick out of the rock when the mould is removed; casts may retain great detail of the outer surface of the specimen, but all internal detail is lost	fairly common

(continued)

Group of processes	Process	Results	Frequency
traces of animal activities	tracks or trails – footprints of vertebrates or trails of invertebrates	tracks and trails are preserved as moulds or casts, preserving details of how the animal moved	trails common, tracks uncommon
	burrows	burrows in which soft- or hard-bodied organisms lived are preserved	fairly common
	coprolites – fossilised faeces	details of the diet and structure of the gut may be preserved	uncommon
	borings – holes drilled by animals; toothmarks	boring is into hard rock and cuts right through any layers (whereas burrows into soft sediment deform layers); animals bore to make holes in which to live or in predation; tooth marks indicate predation	uncommon

3.2N.23   Map of the Earth's tectonic plates

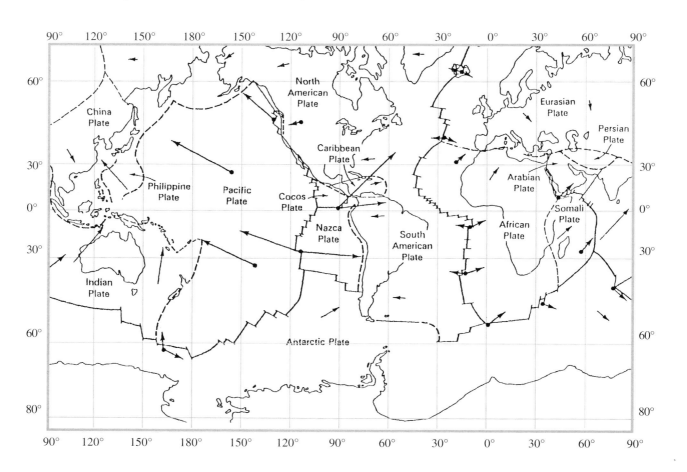

3.2N.24   Fault and fold nomenclature

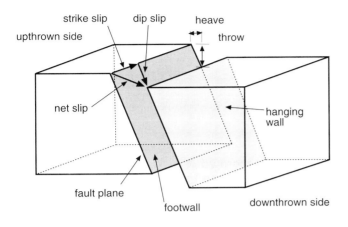

Components of a fault

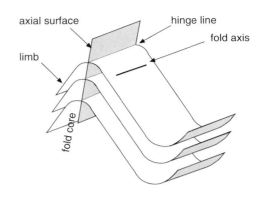

Components of a fold

3.3   Safety

3.3.1   Fire extinguishers

A recent European Standard requires that the body of ALL fire extinguishers shall be coloured red. In addition a zone of colour occupying up to 5% of the external area of the body may be used to identify the extinguishing agent.

In the UK these colours are as listed below.

Colour code	Contents
red	water
blue	dry powder
cream	foam
black	carbon dioxide, CO_2
green	vaporising liquids (such as BCF)

3.3.2   Gas cylinders

Contents	Basic/shoulder colour	Comment/nature
oxygen	black	
nitrogen	grey with black shoulder	
hydrogen	bright red	N.B. screw thread for fitting the regulator is anti-clockwise
carbon dioxide	black	cylinders which release liquid carbon dioxide (for dry ice) have two vertical white stripes
propane	bright red	bearing words 'Propane' and 'Highly Flammable'
acetylene	maroon	ethyne
helium	brown with beige shoulder	balloon gas

3.3.3 Pipes

Contents	Basic colour	Use/nature	Coloured band
water	green	drinking	blue
water	green	central heating <100 °C	blue/crimson/blue
water	green	central heating >100 °C	crimson/blue/crimson
water	green	cold	white/blue/white
water	green	hot	white/crimson/white
water	green	fire-extinguishing	red
fuel gas	yellow ochre	natural gas yellow	
air	light blue		
electrical conduit	orange		

3.3.4 Standards on eye protection

For protection against	British Standard	European Standard	Comments
low velocity impact	BS 2092 2	EN166.F	typical school science safety spectacles
medium velocity impact	BS 2092 1	EN166.B	not usually needed in school science
chemical splash	BS 2092 C	EN166.3	goggles for school science use need at least the suffix C or 3
dust	BS 2092 D	EN166.4	
molten metal	BS 2092 M	EN166.9	

Note: Although eye protection labelled with a British Standard number is still perfectly accceptable for use, all new purchases will be marked 'BS EN 166 ...' to signify UK agreement with the European standard.

4 ELECTRICAL CIRCUIT SYMBOLS

4.1 Component symbols

The electronics symbols used here are BSI Standard – see publications PP7303/86/2k/B (BS3939).

4.1.1 Conduction

current direction, energy or signal flow

conductors crossing with no connection

junction of conductors (dot recommended)

double junction of conductors (dots recommended)

antenna, or aerial wire

earth or ground

frame or chassis connection

make contact, normally open, general switch symbol

break contact

relay coil

4.1.2 Cells

primary or secondary cell

battery of cells, form 1

battery of cells, form 2 – note nominal voltage

open terminals

4.1.3 Resistors, connectors and indicators

plug (male)

socket (female)

indicator or light source

neon indicator

fuse

heater

fixed resistor

potentiometer

4.1.4   Capacitors and inductors

capacitor

polarised capacitor

inductor

inductor with magnetic core

transformer with magnetic core

4.1.5   Meters and detectors

(A)	ammeter	☐	earphone
(V)	voltmeter		loudspeaker
(↑)	galvanometer		electric bell
(~)	oscilloscope		buzzer
W	wattmeter	(M)	motor
– ⋁ +	thermocouple	G	generator
◖◯	microphone		

4.1.6   Solid-state devices

Circles around these devices are optional.

▷⊢	semiconductor diode	▷⊢	photodiode
▷⊢	light-emitting diode	▷⊢	triode thyristor
▷⊢	zener breakdown diode		pnp transistor
⊣⊢	photovoltaic cell		npn transistor
▭	light dependent resistor		

⊣⊢ MOSFET, enhancement type, single gate, n-type channel *without* substrate connection brought out

⊣⊢ MOSFET, enhancement type, single gate, p-type channel *with* substrate connection brought out

⊣⊢ MOSFET, depletion type, single gate, n-type channel *without* substrate connection

⊣⊢ MOSFET, depletion type, single gate, p-type channel *without* substrate connection

4.1.7 Symbols showing variability

Variability can be added to resistive, capacitive or inductive symbols as indicated below,

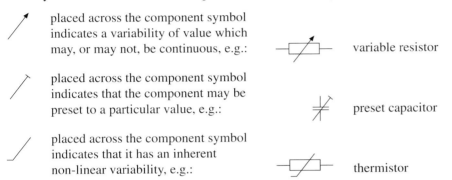

↗ placed across the component symbol indicates a variability of value which may, or may not, be continuous, e.g.:   variable resistor

↗ placed across the component symbol indicates that the component may be preset to a particular value, e.g.:   preset capacitor

↗ placed across the component symbol indicates that it has an inherent non-linear variability, e.g.:   thermistor

4.1.8 Resistor colour codes

This code is a series of four coloured bands around the body of a resistor. The first two represent the digits of the value and the third the multiplier. The fourth ring usually gives the tolerance, but in the case of a five-band code the first three give the digits, the fourth the multiplier and the fifth the tolerance.

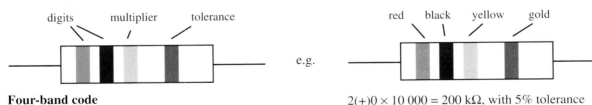

e.g.

Four-band code

$2(+)0 \times 10\ 000 = 200\ k\Omega$, with 5% tolerance

Colour	Digit	Multiplier
black	0	0
brown	1	10
red	2	100
orange	3	1 000
yellow	4	10 000
green	5	100 000
blue	6	1 000 000
violet	7	10 000 000
grey	8	100 000 000
white	9	1 000 000 000

Colour	Tolerance	
no band	+/-	20%
silver	+/-	10%
gold	+/-	5%
red	+/-	2%
brown	+/-	1%

4.1.9   Preferred values

Since exact values of fixed resistors are unnecessary in most circuits only certain preferred values are made. The values chosen for the E24 series (with +/– 5% tolerance) are shown in the table.

These values give maximum coverage with minimum overlap with the +/– 5% tolerance.

E24 series resistor values	Tolerance
1.0, 1.1, 1.2, 1.3, 1.5, 1.6, 1.8	all +/– 5%
2.0, 2.2, 2.4, 2.7	
3.0, 3.3, 3.6, 3.9	
4.3, 4.7	
5.1, 5.6	
6.2, 6.8	
7.5	
8.8	
9.1	
and multiples that are powers of ten greater	

4.1.10   Capacitor colour codes

For non-electrolytic capacitors (e.g. polyester and ceramic) the basic unit is the picofarad. Capacitors are marked with three or four spots or bands. These are read from top to bottom, or left to right, as appropriate. An arrow may be used to indicate the direction, or a blob of paint may indicate the left-hand end.

The digits and multiplier use the same colour as for resistors, but the tolerances use a different code.

Capacitor colour code	Tolerance
black	+/–20%
brown	+/–1%
red	+/–2%
orange	+/–3%
green	+/–5%
white	+/–10%

4.2   Power supplies

A circuit diagram may show either the power supply itself or the points (small open rings) to which the power supply is attached.

4.2.1   dc supplies

The diagrams below illustrate six of the possible ways of drawing a dc power supply in the left-hand current pathway in a circuit diagram.

Notice that the power or signal source is placed on the left, so that the components are on the right. Conventional current (cc) flow should be clockwise.

4.2.2   ac supplies

The next diagram shows an ac supply of frequency 50 Hz and of root mean square magnitude 240 V with the neutral lead at the bottom.

In ac circuits the lower conducting pathway is neutral or earthed.

4.3 Representation of physical variables

The accepted convention is that symbols representing physical variables should be printed in *italic*. UPPER-CASE letters are used to represent constant quantities, and lower case letters are used to represent quantities that vary, for example with time. Any subscripts, which are used are printed in roman (normal upright) type. If two letters are used in a subscript, the second refers to a reference point (such as earth connection) whilst the first refers to the point to which the measurement is made. For example:

$V_{AB} = 6\ V$

$v_{ab} = V_{ab} \sin \omega t = 2 \sin 100\pi t$

$v_{AB} = V_{AB} + v_{ab}$

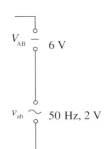

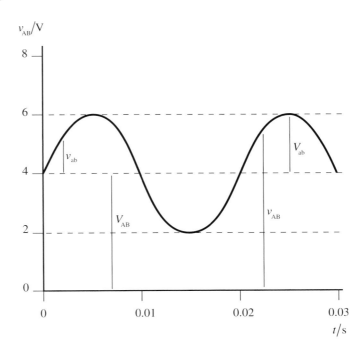

4.4 Electronics

4.4.1 Block diagrams

In the design of electronic circuits block diagrams are used to represent a chunk of the circuit, rather like 'electronic Lego bricks'. The three main blocks are for the input, processor and output circuits.

The blocks identify the principal parts of the circuit and the order in which they are connected together, without giving their constructional details which would enable the circuit to be built. Power supplies or signal sources should be on the left and the output devices should be on the right. Power or signal flow should be from left to right. An example of a burglar alarm is shown below.

A more complex system, involving the use of feedback, may be represented as follows:

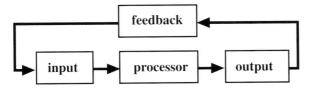

For example, consider a system to maintain a constant temperature in a room. The input could be from a temperature sensor and the processor could be a comparator. The output could be a heater and the feedback would be the heat received by the temperature sensor.

4.4.2 Analogue electronics

Most analogue circuits use the components listed in 4.1. At this level the most common analogue electronic device to be introduced is the operational amplifier or op-amp.

The table here summarises the properties of the ideal op-amp as compared to a real device.

Properties	Ideal op-amp	Real op-amp
input impedance	infinite	$10^{12}\,\Omega$
output impedance	zero	$100\,\Omega$
open loop gain	infinite	94 dB
slew rate	infinite	$13\,\text{V}\,\mu\text{s}^{-1}$

(i) Basic op-amp

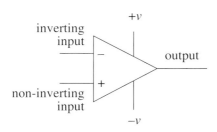

(ii) Voltage follower

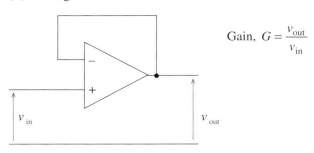

$$\text{Gain, } G = \frac{v_{\text{out}}}{v_{\text{in}}}$$

(iii) Inverting amplifier

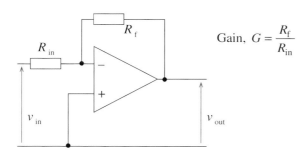

$$\text{Gain, } G = \frac{R_{\text{f}}}{R_{\text{in}}}$$

(iv) Non-inverting amplifier

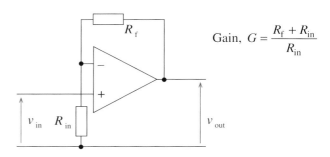

$$\text{Gain, } G = \frac{R_{\text{f}} + R_{\text{in}}}{R_{\text{in}}}$$

(v) Summing amplifier

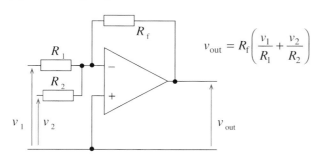

$$v_{\text{out}} = R_{\text{f}}\left(\frac{v_1}{R_1} + \frac{v_2}{R_2}\right)$$

(vi) Differential amplifier

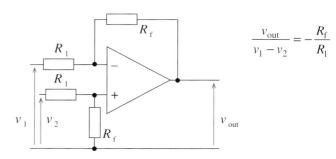

$$\frac{v_{\text{out}}}{v_1 - v_2} = -\frac{R_{\text{f}}}{R_1}$$

4.4.3 Digital electronics

The symbols shown below are those of the American ANSI Y 32.14 (1973), which have gained almost universal acceptance in educational work.

AND gate	Truth table	A	B	Q
A B Q		0	0	0
		0	1	0
		1	0	0
		1	1	1

OR gate		A	B	Q
A B Q		0	0	0
		0	1	1
		1	0	1
		1	1	1

NAND gate		A	B	Q
A B Q		0	0	1
		0	1	1
		1	0	1
		1	1	0

NOR gate		A	B	Q
A B Q		0	0	1
		0	1	0
		1	0	0
		1	1	0

EX-OR gate		A	B	Q
A B Q		0	0	0
		0	1	1
		1	0	1
		1	1	0

NOT gate (inverter)		A		Q
A Q		0		1
		1		0

4.4.4 Boolean algebra: rules for algebra for binary numbers

(i) Inputs are A, B or C and the output is Q. $\overline{A}$ or $\overline{Q}$ means the inverse or opposite of A and Q (thus if A = 1, $\overline{A}$ = 0).

(ii) A.B means A AND B, whereas A+B means A OR B.

(iii) With combinations of logic gates, 'post-operation' by NOT (i.e. NOT at the output) inverts a gate, but 'pre-operation' by NOT (i.e. NOT inverting each input) turns AND to OR and inverts the gate to NOR.

(iv) De Morgan's rule: To obtain the complement of a Boolean expression, complement each variable and exchange AND for OR (and vice-versa).

(v) Logic gates:

AND: $Q = A.B$

OR: $Q = A + B$

NAND: $Q = \overline{A.B}$ and $Q = \overline{A} + \overline{B}$

NOR: $Q = \overline{A + B}$ and $Q = \overline{A}.\overline{B}$

4.4.5 Diagrams of circuits

(i) 555 Timer IC
10 kΩ variable alters frequency

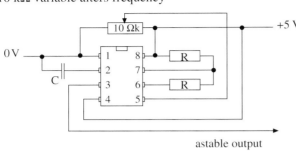

astable output

(ii) Monostable

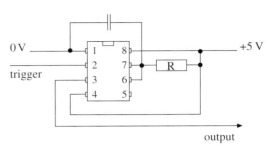

output

(iii) Schmitt trigger and NOT gate

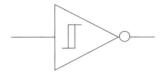

(iv) D-type latch

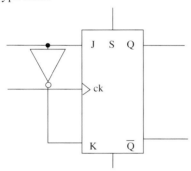

or

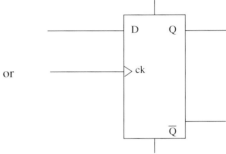

(v) Binary counter (4-bit)

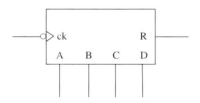

(vi) Simple microprocessor system – block diagram

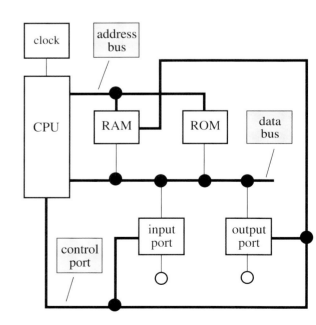

4.5   Formulae

For resistance R, capacitance C, time constant T
(if R is in kΩ and C in mF, then T is in ms)

$$T = R \times C$$

Capacitor discharging from maximum voltage V_0
(likewise I and Q)

$$V = V_0 e^{-t/RC}$$

Capacitor charging to a maximum voltage V_0
(likewise I and Q)

$$V = V_0(1 - e^{-t/RC})$$

For sinusoidal ac waveforms, peak current I_p

$$I_{rms} = \frac{I_p}{\sqrt{2}}$$

For sinusoidal ac waveforms, peak voltage V_p

$$V_{rms} = \frac{V_p}{\sqrt{2}}$$

For half-wave rectified supply, mean voltage V_{mean}

$$V_{mean} = \frac{V_p}{\pi}$$

For full-wave rectified supply, mean voltage V_{mean}

$$V_{mean} = \frac{2V_p}{\pi}$$

Ripple voltage (full-wave rectified supply) ΔV

$$\Delta V = \frac{V \Delta \tau}{RC}$$

Capacitance reactance X_C

$$X_C = \frac{1}{2\pi f C}$$

Inductive reactance X_L

$$X_L = 2\pi f L$$

Total impedance

$$Z^2 = R^2 + (X_L - X_C)^2$$

Resonant frequency f_r

$$f_r = \frac{1}{2\pi\sqrt{LC}}$$

Break frequency (for filters) f

$$f = \frac{1}{2\pi RC}$$

555 timer, for monostable, T

$$T = \frac{(R_1 + R_2)C_1}{1.44}$$

Voltage gain G

$$G = \frac{\Delta V_{out}}{\Delta V_{in}}$$

Closed loop gain for an op-amp with open loop gain A_0,
feedback factor β

$$A = \frac{A_0}{1 + \beta A_0}$$

5 CHEMICAL NOMENCLATURE: INORGANIC

5.1 General introduction

This section describes the systems for naming inorganic compounds. Names can be *trivial* or *systematic*. Trivial names such as 'starch' or 'litmus' serve to identify what is in a bottle. Systematic names not only identify what is in the bottle but also give more information about the composition and molecular structure of the substance. Systematic names are usually longer or more complicated than trivial names, because they carry much more information: the trivial name 'Glauber's salt' is shorter than 'sodium sulfate-10-water' but also tells us less. The systematic name and the formula of a compound are closely related. If the detailed formula of a compound is important and meaningful to the student, we should use the systematic name but temper the complexity of the name to the needs of the student (see 'copper(II) sulfate(VI)' in Section 5.3.2).

5.2 Rules for naming inorganic compounds

5.2.1 Binary inorganic compounds

Compounds containing two elements have names ending in '-ide', with the more electropositive element named first. For example, MgO is 'magnesium oxide' but OF_2 is 'oxygen difluoride'. (The hydroxides and cyanides break this rule – there are historical reasons for these names.)

The chief exceptions are water, ammonia, methane and other non-metal hydrides. There has been a suggestion that ammonia should be named 'azane' but this name has not yet been adopted widely. The terms halide, hydroxide and cyanide continue in use. The oxidation number of the less electronegative constituent is indicated by a Roman numeral in parentheses after the name of that element (e.g. copper(II) oxide, tin(IV) oxide, phosphorus(V) oxide) unless the compound consists of simple molecules whose composition is known (e.g. phosphorus trichloride, PCl_3; oxygen difluoride, OF_2; sulfur dioxide, SO_2), in which case the stoichiometry determines the name. The order, in the case of binary compounds between non-metals, is according to the sequence:
Rn, Xe, Kr, B, Si, C, Sb, As, P, N, H, Te, Se, S, At, I, Br, Cl, O, F

The symbol for the earlier constituent is placed first and that for the later (i.e. more electronegative) constituent follows it.

If the molecular complexity is variable, the simplest ratio is taken as the name of the equilibrium mixture (e.g. nitrogen dioxide rather than dinitrogen tetraoxide). In accordance with their chemistry, arsenic compounds are named in the same way as phosphorus compounds while antimony and bismuth are treated in their compounds as metals.

The dicarbide CaC_2 and other metallic derivatives of ethyne are usually named on the basis of organic nomenclature. The name used will, however, depend on the context, which is sometimes purely inorganic.

5.2.2 'Stock' notation

In compounds which are not molecular, such as ionic or polymeric solids, the oxidation state of the electropositive element is given in Roman numerals unless there can be no doubt about what it is. 'Sodium chloride' is so named rather than 'sodium(I) chloride' because the only sodium ion is Na^+. 'Copper(II) chloride' is so named because copper(I) chloride also exists. In borderline cases, such as 'silver nitrate', the teacher must decide on the student's behalf whether to admit to the existence of a few silver(II) compounds or to avoid over-sophistication.

5.2.3 Simple salts

The number of possible combinations of well-known ions clearly precludes the listing of all those likely to be met at this age group. For guidance in indexing and storing, fuller coverage of aluminium and ammonium salts is given in Section 5.3A. Other compounds can be named by analogy, using the listed names of the constituent ions.

5.2.4 Double salts

In a double salt there are two cations but these are independent of each other (i.e. they do not join together to form a complex, though each might be hydrated). One example is the series of 'alums', of which 'aluminium potassium sulfate(VI)-12-water', $AlK(SO_4)_2.12H_2O$, is the best known. Less commonly, there can be more than one anion.

The order of naming is that cations precede anions and within each category the ions are listed in alphabetical order of their names. In writing chemical formulae, however, the sequence within each class should be in alphabetical order of the symbols (except that hydrogen is always cited last, before the anion).

Thus:

chromium(III) potassium sulfate(VI)-12-water	$CrK(SO_4)_2.12H_2O$
pentasilver(I) dibromide dichloride iodide	$Ag_5Br_2Cl_2I$
ammonium chromium(III) sulfate(VI)-12-water	$CrNH_4(SO_4)_2.12H_2O$ (because Cr precedes N alphabetically)
hexasodium chloride fluoride bis(sulfate(VI))	$Na_6ClF(SO_4)_2$ (See Section 6.2.6. 'bis' is used because 'sulfate(VI)' could be named at greater length 'tetraoxosulfate(VI)' and a name such as 'di(tetraoxo...)' would be clumsy. 'bisulfate(VI)' and 'disulfate(VI)' are also used in other contexts.)
sodium hydrogensulfate(VI)	$NaHSO_4$
bismuth(III) chloride oxide	$BiClO$

Basic salts are named, as in the last example, as double salts with O^{2-} or OH^- anions whenever the structure is known. The same procedure is used with double oxides, such as dichromium(III) copper(II) oxide, Cr_2CuO_4; this name denotes the formula more accurately than would the name 'copper(II) chromate(III)' for the material formerly known as copper chromite. Substances of variable composition may be written as, for example, 'Ag(Br,Cl)' (for a mixed precipitate of silver ions with both anions).

There is a system of nomenclature in which these compounds are termed 'Addition compounds' and named as, for example, 'sodium chloride – sodium fluoride – sodium sulfate(VI) – (1/1/2)' but the Working Party does not consider it to be suitable for the 16–19 age group.

5.2.5 Coordination compounds

Many metal ions exist in aqueous solution as 'complexes' in which the cation is surrounded by and bonded to several water molecules (usually six). If the formula of the complex is important to the student it should be named systematically.

For example: the iron(III) cation in aqueous solution, $Fe^{3+}(aq)$, has formula $[Fe(H_2O)_6]^{3+}$ and is therefore named the 'hexaaquairon(III) ion' (hexa = 6, aqua = H_2O, iron(III) = Fe^{3+}). There is no hyphen between 'hexa' and 'aqua' but the syllables are spoken with a slight break between them and not run together as 'hexaqua'. (There is a similar break in 'coordination', in which the two sounds 'o' are not run together as '-oo-'.)

If the complex contains ammonia (such as the result of adding excess aqueous ammonia to copper(II) sulfate(VI) solution), the NH_3 is named as '-ammine'. A complex can be negatively charged and, if so, its name ends in '-ate' like the salts of oxoacids. For example, the ion $[Fe(CN)_6]^{3-}$ is 'hexacyanoferrate(III)'. The iron ion is named by its Latin name (ferrum) and its oxidation state, still +3, given. This complex used to be known as

'ferricyanide', which gives less information than the systematic name.

In general, for the purpose of nomenclature, coordination compounds are treated as consisting of a 'central' atom to which 'ligands' (atoms, ions or groups) are attached to form a 'complex'. The name of the complex is formed by placing the names of the ligands in alphabetical order, ignoring numerical prefixes, before the name of the central atom. The oxidation number of the central atom is placed after the metal name for a cation and after the metal name and the suffix '-ate' for an anion. Thus:

tetracarbonylnickel(0)	$Ni(CO)_4$
tetraamminecopper(II)	$Cu(NH_3)_4^{2+}$
hexafluoroaluminate(III)	AlF_6^{3-}
pentacyanonitrosylferrate(II)	$[Fe(CN)_5(NO)]^{2-}$

The total charge on the complex may be deduced from the name.

It is recommended that oxidation numbers should not be used in relation to carbon.

5.2.6   Hydrates

The name of the anhydrous substance is followed successively by a hyphen, the stoichiometric proportion stated as an arabic number, a hyphen and the word 'water' (thus: 'copper(II) sulfate(VI)-5-water'). The formula of this is written as $CuSO_4.5H_2O$, with the point on the line. When the extent of hydration is uncertain, the word 'hydrated' may be placed before the name of the anhydrous substance. In advanced work, when the structure is known and if it is important to the student, the attachment of water molecules may be shown using coordination nomenclature (e.g. tetraaquacopper(II) sulfate(VI)-1-water).

5.2.7   Inorganic oxoacids

Oxoacids (not 'oxy-') and their salts used to be named as '...-ic acid' (name of salt ending in '-ate') and '...-ous acid' (name of salt ending in '-ite'), with the former containing more oxygen. The two examples still used in schools up to age 16 are nitric/nitrous acids (salts nitrates/nitrites) and sulfuric/sulfurous acids (salts sulfates/sulfites). Many people will continue to use these names for the 16+ group.

Systematically '-ic'(and '-ate') are used for all oxoacids (and their salts), giving the oxidation number of the central atom. Thus:

H_2SO_4 is sulfuric(VI) acid

H_2SO_3 is sulfuric(IV) acid

HNO_3 is nitric(V) acid

HNO_2 is nitric(III) acid.

The four oxoacids of chlorine are:

$HClO$, chloric(I) acid

$HClO_2$, chloric(III) acid

$HClO_3$, chloric(V) acid

$HClO_4$, chloric(VII) acid   (instead of hypochlorous, chlorous, chloric and perchloric, respectively).

In systematic names the ending '-ate' does *not* imply the highest oxidation state of the central atom.

The term 'peroxoacid' is used only for those acids containing the group –O–O–.

The systematic names of oxoanions are formed in the same way as those of other anionic complexes, e.g. tetraoxomanganate(VII), and can be for the eight acids named above, if this is needed.

Acid salts are named as, for example, sodium dihydrogenphosphate(V). Basic salts are named as double salts with O^{2-} or OH^- anions whenever the structure is known (thus: bismuth(III) chloride oxide).

5.3 Systematic names for inorganic species

5.3.1 Notes

1 The recommended name given here is that recommended for general use and for labelling substances, and is a systematic name. Other names given in parentheses are more detailed systematic names appropriate to advanced study of structures or are suitable in some particular context which is stated. Hyphens are not recommended by IUPAC to separate double 'a', etc. (e.g. in 'hexaaqua') but they may be used if desired for clarity.

2 In this section the symbol * after a name indicates that the composition is indefinite or the structure complicated: a full systematic name and structural formula are considered inappropriate for the 16–19 age range.

3 Aluminium and ammonium compounds are more fully listed than those of other cations for which the corresponding compounds are named by analogy.

4 'Traditional' names are given only when they are markedly different from the systematic name recommended.

5 Multiplying prefixes (such as di-, tri-, tetra-) have been disregarded in arranging the names in alphabetical order, except in certain cases, e.g. dichromate(VI), disulfate(IV) and dithionate, where the situation is more complicated.

6 Oxidation numbers are retained in fully systematic names for complex ions but may be omitted in the case of Al, Si, Zn, etc., if desired.

7 Chemical formulae are omitted for elements, ions of indefinite constitution and complicated substances, when the formula would not need to be known by the 16–19 age group.

8 In ions such as OCN^-, SCN^-, the formula does not indicate the location of the charge, which is considered to be delocalised.

5.3.2 Recommended names: inorganic

Recommended name	Traditional name	Formula
aluminate ion*		AlO_2^-
aluminium		
(names of elements are usually not listed. British spelling of aluminium is retained.)		
aluminium ion		Al^{3+}
(in aqueous solution, the hexaaquaaluminium(III) ion will coexist with ions such as pentaaquahydroxoaluminium(III) ion, etc.)		
aluminium ammonium sulfate(VI)-12-water	ammonium alum	$AlNH_4(SO_4)_2.12H_2O$
aluminium(III) bromide		$AlBr_3$
(this name implies the stoichiometry but not the molecular formula. If it is necessary to refer to molecules in the vapour state, the words 'monomer' or 'dimer' may be added. If conditions are not given, room temperature and pressure are implied, for which this compound is a dimer.)		
aluminium hydroxide		$Al(OH)_3$
aluminium nitrate(V)		$Al(NO_3)_3$
aluminium oxide		Al_2O_3
aluminium oxide (corundum)	corundum	
(other minerals should be named in a similar manner)		
aluminium phosphate(V)		$AlPO_4$
aluminium potassium sulfate(VI)-12-water	alum	$AlK(SO_4)_2.12H_2O$
aluminium sulfate(VI)		$Al_2(SO_4)_3$
tetraamminecopper(II) ion	cuprammonium ion	$[Cu(NH_3)_4]^{2+}$
(other ammines are named similarly. Strictly, this ion is the tetraamminebisaqua copper(II) ion, $[Cu(NH_3)_4(H_2O)_2]^{2+}$)		
ammonia	ammonia gas	NH_3
(see also 'aqueous ammonia')		
ammoniacal silver(I) nitrate(V)		
(see note on 'silver ion')		
ammonium ion		NH_4^+
ammonium benzenecarboxylate (or benzoate)	ammonium benzoate	$NH_4C_6H_5CO_2$
ammonium cerium(IV) sulfate(VI)	ammonium ceric sulphate	$Ce(NH_4)_4(SO_4)_4$
ammonium copper(II) sulfate(VI)-6-water	ammonium cupric sulphate	$Cu(NH_4)_2(SO_4)_2$
ammonium dichromate(VI)		$(NH_4)_2Cr_2O_7$
ammonium dihydrogenphosphate(V)	ammonium dihydrogenorthophosphate	$NH_4H_2PO_4$
ammonium ethanedioate	ammonium oxalate	$(NH_4)_2C_2O_4$

---

*   Composition indefinite or structure complicated: see note 2, Section 5.3.1.
n.c. No change.

Recommended name	Traditional name	Formula
ammonium ethanoate	ammonium acetate	$NH_4CH_3CO_2$
ammonium hydrogencarbonate	ammonium bicarbonate	NH_4HCO_3
ammonium hydrogenphosphate(V)		$(NH_4)_2HPO_4$
ammonium hydrogensulfate(VI)	ammonium bisulphate	NH_4HSO_4
ammonium iron(II) sulfate(VI)-6-water	ferrous ammonium sulphate	$Fe(NH_4)_2(SO_4)_2.6H_2O$
ammonium iron(III) sulfate(VI)-12-water	ferric alum	$FeNH_4(SO_4)_2.12H_2O$
ammonium methanoate	ammonium formate	NH_4HCO_2
ammonium nickel(II) sulfate(VI)-6-water		$(NH_4)_2Ni(SO_4)_2.6H_2O$
ammonium nitrate(V)		NH_4NO_3
ammonium peroxodisulfate(VI)	ammonium persulphate	$(NH_4)_2S_2O_8$
ammonium phosphate(V)	ammonium orthophosphate	$(NH_4)_3PO_4$
ammonium polytrioxovanadate(V)	ammonium metavanadate	NH_4VO_3
ammonium sodium hydrogenphosphate(V)		$Na(NH_4)HPO_4$
ammonium sulfate(VI)		$(NH_4)_2SO_4$
ammonium thiocyanate		NH_4SCN
antimony(III) chloride	antimony trichloride	$SbCl_3$
antimony(III) oxide	antimony trioxide	Sb_2O_3
antimony(V) oxide	antimony pentoxide	Sb_2O_5
hexaaquaaluminium ion	hydrated aluminium ion	$[Al(H_2O)_6]^{3+}$

(other hydrated cations are named similarly when a definite structure is to be indicated. More generally, terms such as 'aqueous aluminium ion' or 'hydrated aluminium ion' are used.)

hexaaquacopper(II) ion		$[Cu(H_2O)_6]^{2+}$
aqueous ammonia	ammonium hydroxide	$NH_3(aq)$

(representations such as NH_4OH should not be used to denote the mixture of species present)

aqueous calcium hydroxide	limewater	$Ca(OH)_2(aq)$
arsine		AsH_3
asbestos		
azide ion		N_3^-

barium ion		Ba^{2+}
barium peroxide		BaO_2
bismuth(III) ion		Bi^{3+}
bismuth(III) chloride	bismuth trichloride	$BiCl_3$
bismuth(III) chloride oxide	bismuthyl chloride; bismuth oxychloride	$BiClO$
bleaching powder*		

(it is incorrect to describe this as calcium chlorate(I) or calcium hypochlorite. It is correct to describe it as 'containing calcium ions, chloride ions, chlorate(I) ions and water'.)

borate ion*

(in dilute solutions the tetrahydroxoborate(III) ion predominates. At higher concentrations, condensed ions such as tetrahydroxotrioxoborate(III) occur.)

boric acid*		H_3BO_3

(the name trioxoboric(III) acid correctly describes the solid acid and its dilute solutions. Condensed acids occur in more concentrated solutions. $(HBO_2)_n$ is named polydioxoboric(III) acid.)

boron(III) oxide*		B_2O_3
boron trifluoride		BF_3

(the oxide is of uncertain molecular formula, whereas the halide consists of simple molecules which are accurately described by the name above)

bromate(I) ion (fully, oxobromate(I) ion)	hypobromite ion	BrO^-
bromate(V) ion (fully, trioxobromate(V) ion)	bromate ion	BrO_3^-
bromic(I) acid (fully, oxobromic(I) acid)	hypobromous acid	$HBrO$
bromic(V) acid (fully, trioxobromic acid)	bromic acid	$HBrO_3$
bromine trifluoride		BrF_3

* Composition indefinite or structure complicated: see note 2, Section 5.3.1
n.c. No change.

Recommended name	Traditional name	Formula
cadmium ion		Cd^{2+}
caesium ion		Cs^+
calcium ion		Ca^{2+}
calcium carbonate		$CaCO_3$
calcium carbonate (calcite)	calcite	
calcium carbonate (limestone)	limestone	
calcium ethynediide or calcium dicarbide	calcium acetylide; calcium carbide	CaC_2
(the name used will depend on the context: see 5.2.1)		
calcium hydroxide	slaked lime	$Ca(OH)_2$
calcium octadecanoate	calcium stearate	$Ca(C_{17}H_{35}CO_2)_2$
calcium oxide	quicklime	CaO
carbide ion		C^{4-}
(this means the ion C^{4-} as in Al_4C_3. The ion C_2^{2-} is the dicarbide ion or ethynediide ion according to context. See Section 5.2.1.)		
carbon (animal charcoal)	animal charcoal	
carbon (diamond)	diamond	
carbon (fullerene)	buckminsterfullerene	
carbon (graphite)	graphite	
carbon (wood charcoal)	wood charcoal	
(other materials having forms differing in purity or crystal structure are described in the same manner.)		
carbon dioxide		CO_2
carbon monoxide		CO
carbonate ion		CO_3^{2-}
pentacarbonyliron(0)	iron pentacarbonyl	$Fe(CO)_5$
tetracarbonylnickel(0)	nickel carbonyl	$Ni(CO)_4$
cerate(IV) ion*	cerate ion	
cerium(III) ion	cerous ion	Ce^{3+}
cerium(IV) ion	ceric ion	Ce^{4+}
chlorate(I) ion	hypochlorite ion	ClO^-
(fully, oxochlorate(I) ion)		
chlorate(III) ion	chlorite ion	ClO_2^-
(fully, dioxochlorate(III) ion)		
chlorate(V) ion	chlorate ion	ClO_3^-
(fully, trioxochlorate(V) ion)		
chlorate(VII) ion	perchlorate ion	ClO_4^-
(fully, tetraoxochlorate(VII) ion)		
chloric(I) acid	hypochlorous acid	$HClO$
(fully, oxochloric(I) acid)		
chloric(III) acid	chlorous acid	$HClO_2$
(fully, dioxochloric(III) acid)		
chloric(V) acid	chloric acid	$HClO_3$
(fully, trioxochloric(V) acid)		
chloric(VII) acid	perchloric acid	$HClO_4$
(fully, tetraoxochloric(VII) acid)		
chloride ion		Cl^-
chlorine dioxide		ClO_2
dichlorine oxide	chlorine monoxide	Cl_2O
trichlorocuprate(I) ion	cuprochloride ion	$[CuCl_3]^{2-}$
(other ions such as dichlorocuprate(I) are present in aqueous solution)		
tetrachlorocuprate(II) ion	cuprichloride ion	$[CuCl_4]^{2-}$
(other ions such as trichlorocuprate(II) may also be present in aqueous solution)		
tetrachloromethane	carbon tetrachloride	CCl_4
(the name carbon tetrachloride is appropriate in the context of silicon tetrachloride)		
hexachloroplatinate(IV) ion	platinichloride ion	$[PtCl_6]^{2-}$
chromate(III) ion*	chromite ion	

*   Composition indefinite or structure complicated: see note 2, Section 5.3.1.
n.c. No change.

Recommended name	Traditional name	Formula
chromate(VI) ion (fully, tetraoxochromate(VI) ion)	chromate ion	CrO_4^{2-}
chromic(VI) acid (fully described as tetraoxochromic acid, but polychromic acids may well be present)	chromic acid	H_2CrO_4
chromium(II) ion	chromous ion	Cr^{2+}
chromium(III) ion (see note on aluminium ion)	chromic ion	Cr^{3+}
dichromium(III) copper(II) oxide (this name correctly describes the composition. The chromites of alkali metals may, however, be named as chromate(III) compounds.)	copper chromite	Cr_2CuO_4
chromium(VI) dichloride dioxide	chromyl chloride	$CrCl_2O_2$
chromium(VI) oxide	chromium trioxide	CrO_3
chromium(III) potassium sulfate(VI)-12-water	chrome alum	$CrK(SO_4)_2.12H_2O$
cobalt(II) ion	cobaltous ion	Co^{2+}
cobalt(III) ion	cobaltic ion	Co^{3+}
copper(I) ion	cuprous ion	Cu^+
copper(I) chloride	cuprous chloride	$CuCl$
copper(II) ion (see aluminium ion and hexaaquaaluminium for note on hydrates)	cupric ion	Cu^{2+} or $[Cu(H_2O)_6]^{2+}$
copper(II) sulfate(VI) (copper sulfate may be an adequate name for introductory work, whilst hydrated copper sulfate may be used later. The familiar blue crystals are fully described as tetraaquacopper(II) tetraoxosulfate(VI)-1-water although copper(II) sulfate-5-water will often be the most appropriate name.)	cupric sulphate	$CuSO_4$ $CuSO_4.5H_2O$
cyanate ion		OCN^-
cyanide ion		CN^-
hexacyanoferrate(II) ion	ferrocyanide ion	$[Fe(CN)_6]^{4-}$
hexacyanoferrate(III) ion	ferricyanide ion	$[Fe(CN)_6]^{3-}$
cyanogen		C_2N_2
dichromate(VI) ion (fully, heptaoxodichromate(VI) ion)	dichromate ion	$Cr_2O_7^{2-}$
disulfate(IV) ion (fully, pentaoxodisulfate(IV) ion)	metabisulphite ion	$S_2O_5^{2-}$
dithionate ion		$S_2O_6^{2-}$
tetraethyllead(IV)	lead tetraethyl	$Pb(C_2H_5)_4$
fluoride ion		F^-
hexafluoroaluminate(III) ion (present in the mineral cryolite; the oxidation number may be omitted)		$[AlF_6]^{3-}$
germanium(IV) oxide*		GeO_2
hydrazine		N_2H_4
hydrazinium chloride	hydrazine hydrochloride	N_2H_5Cl
hydride ion		H^-
tetrahydridoaluminate(III) ion (the oxidation number may be omitted)	aluminohydride ion	$[AlH_4]^-$
tetrahydridoborate(III) ion (the oxidation number may be omitted)	borohydride ion	$[BH_4]^-$
hydriodic acid		$HI(aq)$
hydrobromic acid		$HBr(aq)$
hydrochloric acid		$HCl(aq)$
hydrofluoric acid		$HF(aq)$

*   Composition indefinite or structure complicated: see note 2, Section 5.3.1.
n.c. No change.

Recommended name	Traditional name	Formula
hydrogen		

(isotopes may be distinguished as ^1_1H (protium), ^2_1H (deuterium), ^3_1H (tritium). The molecule H_2 is named dihydrogen when it is required to distinguish it from monohydrogen. The name 'hydrogen' implies the naturally-occurring isotopic composition.)

Recommended name	Traditional name	Formula
hydrogen ion (but see oxonium ion)		H^+
hydrogen bromide		HBr
hydrogen chloride		HCl
hydrogen fluoride		HF
hydrogen iodide		HI
hydrogen peroxide		H_2O_2
hydrogencarbonate ion	bicarbonate ion	HCO_3^-
hydrogendifluoride ion	hydrogen fluoride ion	HF_2^-
hydrogenethanedioate ion	binoxalate ion	$HC_2O_4^-$
hydrogenphosphate(v) ion		HPO_4^{2-}
dihydrogenphosphate(v) ion		$H_2PO_4^-$
hydrogensulfate(vi) ion	bisulphate ion	HSO_4^-
hydrogensulfide ion	hydrosulphide ion	HS^-
hydrogensulfate(iv) ion	bisulphite ion	HSO_3^-
hydroxide ion		OH^-
hydroxo- (a ligand)		HO in e.g. borate ion
hydroxyl group		OH
hydroxylamine		NH_2OH
hydroxylammonium ion		$HONH_3^+$

(terms such as hydroxylamine hydrochloride are deprecated)

Recommended name	Traditional name	Formula
iodate(v) ion (fully, trioxoiodate(v) ion)	iodate ion	IO_3^-
iodate(vii) ion (fully, tetraoxoiodate(vii) ion)	periodate ion	IO_4^-
iodic(v) acid (fully, trioxoiodic acid)	iodic acid	HIO_3
iodic(vii) acid (fully, tetraoxoiodic(vii) acid)	periodic acid	HIO_4
iodide ion		I^-
iodine(i) ion	iodonium ion	I^+
iodine monochloride		ICl

(used for clarity, though IUPAC prefers iodine chloride)

Recommended name	Traditional name	Formula
iron(ii) ion	ferrous ion	Fe^{2+}
iron(ii) diiron(iii) oxide	ferrosoferric oxide	$Fe^{II}(Fe^{III})_2O_4$
	or magnetite	or Fe_3O_4
iron(ii) disulfide (pyrites)	iron pyrites	FeS_2
iron(iii) ion	ferric ion	Fe^{3+}
iron(iii) chloride	ferric chloride	$FeCl_3$

(this name reflects the stoichiometry but not the molecular formula. If it is necessary to refer to molecules in the vapour, the words 'monomer' or 'dimer' may be added. In their absence the name implies the form or mixture stable under the conditions given.)

Recommended name	Traditional name	Formula
lead(ii) ion	plumbous ion	Pb^{2+}
lead(ii) carbonate (cerussite)	cerussite	$PbCO_3$
lead(ii) carbonate hydroxide	white lead	$Pb_2CO_3(OH)_2$
lead(ii) ethanoate	lead acetate	$Pb(CH_3CO_2)_2$
dilead(ii) lead(iv) oxide	red lead	$(Pb^{II})_2Pb^{IV}O_4$
		or Pb_3O_4
lead(ii) oxide (litharge, or massicot)	lead monoxide (litharge, or massicot)	PbO
lead(iv) ethanoate	lead tetraacetate	$Pb(CH_3CO_2)_4$

* Composition indefinite or structure complicated: see note 2, Section 5.3.1.
n.c. No change.

Recommended name	Traditional name	Formula
lead(IV) oxide	lead dioxide	PbO_2
lithium ion		Li^+
lithium tetrahydridoaluminate(III)	lithium aluminium hydride	$Li[AlH_4]$
magnesium ion		Mg^{2+}
manganate(VI) ion (fully, tetraoxomanganate(VI) ion)	manganate ion	MnO_4^{2-}
manganate(VII) ion (fully, tetraoxomanganate(VII) ion)	permanganate ion	MnO_4^-
manganese(II) ion	manganous ion	Mn^{2+}
manganese(III) ion	manganic ion	Mn^{3+}
manganese(IV) oxide	manganese dioxide	MnO_2
manganese(VII) oxide	manganese heptoxide	Mn_2O_7
dimercury(I) ion	mercurous ion	Hg_2^{2+}

(the simpler name mercury(I) ion is unambiguous stoichiometrically though it suggests Hg^+. Some may nevertheless prefer it.)

mercury(II) ion	mercuric ion	Hg^{2+}
monohydrogen	atomic hydrogen	H
mononitrogen	atomic nitrogen	N

(other single atoms similarly, except for helium, neon, etc.)

nickel(II) ion	nickelous ion	Ni^{2+}
nitrate(III) ion (fully, dioxonitrate(III) ion)	nitrite ion	NO_2^-
nitrate(V) ion (fully, trioxonitrate(V) ion)	nitrate ion	NO_3^-
nitric(III) acid (fully, dioxonitric(III) acid)	nitrous acid	HNO_2
nitric(V) acid (fully, trioxonitric(V) acid)	nitric acid	HNO_3
nitride ion		N^{3-}
nitrogen		

(the molecule N_2 is named dinitrogen when it is required to distinguish it from mononitrogen, N)

nitrogen dioxide		NO_2

(unless otherwise indicated, the equilibrium mixture is implied. N_2O_4, as such, is named dinitrogen tetraoxide.)

nitrogen monoxide	nitric oxide	NO

(used for clarity, though IUPAC prefers nitrogen oxide)

dinitrogen oxide	nitrous oxide	N_2O
nitrosyl cation	nitrosyl ion	NO^+
nitryl cation	nitronium ion	NO_2^+

oxoacids	oxyacids	

(the numerical and -oxo- portion of the fully systematic names may, in most cases, be omitted without serious risk of ambiguity, e.g. 'phosphoric(V) acid' rather than 'tetraoxophosphoric(V) acid'.)

oxonium ion	hydronium ion	H_3O^+

(these names refer, strictly, to the H_3O^+ ion. The name hydrogen ion or hydrated hydrogen ion should be used for $H^+(aq)$.)

oxovanadium(IV) ion	vanadyl ion	VO^{2+}
oxygen		

(in discussion of allotropy the name dioxygen should be used to denote O_2)

trioxygen	ozone	O_3

(the term ozonolysis has not been replaced by a more systematic word. Accordingly the name ozone may be required in this context. The name trioxygen should be used when discussing allotropy.)

oxygen difluoride	fluorine monoxide	OF_2

* Composition indefinite or structure complicated: see note 2, Section 5.3.1.
n.c. No change.

Recommended name	Traditional name	Formula
peroxoborate(III) ion	perborate ion	
(many solid so-called perborates contain borate ions and hydrogen peroxide of crystallisation)		
peroxodisulfate(VI) ion	perdisulphate ion	$S_2O_8^{2-}$
phosphate(V) ion	orthophosphate ion	PO_4^{3-}
(fully, tetraoxophosphate(v) ion. In salts, the number of cations will make it clear that phosphate(v) means PO_4^{3-}. In solutions containing a mixture of simple and condensed ions, phosphate(v) can serve to indicate the oxidation number and the full names may be used to distinguish tetraoxophosphate(v) from diphosphate(v), i.e. heptaoxodiphosphate(v).)		
phosphonic acid	phosphorous acid	H_3PO_3, $[HP(=O)(OH)_2]$
(the acid $P(OH)_3$, phosphoric(III) acid, an isomer of phosphonic acid, has not been made. However esters of it do exist.)		
phosphoric(V) acid	orthophosphoric acid	H_3PO_4
(fully, tetraoxophosphoric(v) acid, but see note on phosphate(v) ion)		
phosphorus		
(allotropes may be distinguished as phosphorus(violet) ('red'), phosphorus(black), phosphorus(white) ('yellow') or as polyphosphorus and tetraphosphorus)		
phosphorus(III) oxide*	phosphorus trioxide	P_2O_3
phosphorus trichloride (and other halides)		PCl_3 (etc.)
phosphorus trichloride oxide	phosphorus oxychloride	PCl_3O
phosphorus(V) chloride (and other halides)		PCl_5 (etc.)
(the solid chloride is, strictly, tetrachlorophosphonium hexachlorophosphate(v), whereas the solid pentabromide is, strictly, tetrabromophosphonium bromide. The simple molecules PCl_5 and PBr_5 do exist in the vapour.)		
phosphorus(V) oxide*	phosphorus pentoxide	P_2O_5
(the name tetraphosphorus decaoxide can be used to describe the P_4O_{10} molecule which is present in the vapour. The solid is polymeric so it is appropriate to use the empirical formula P_2O_5.)		
potassium ion		K^+
silane		SiH_4
silicate ion*		
silicon(IV) oxide*	silicon dioxide, silica	SiO_2
(the name silicon dioxide may be appropriate in introductory work)		
silicon tetrachloride		$SiCl_4$
(the oxides are of uncertain molecular formula, whereas the halides consist of simple molecules which are accurately described by names such as silicon tetrachloride)		
silver(I) ion		Ag^+
(it may normally be preferable to use 'silver ion')		
sodium ion		Na^+
sodium aluminate*		
(see note on aluminate ion)		
disodium tetraborate(III)-10-water	borax	$Na_2B_4O_7.10H_2O$
(fully, sodium(I) heptaoxotetraborate(III)-10-water)		
For other sodium compounds, refer either to ammonium compounds or to the appropriate anion.		
strontium ion		Sr^{2+}
sulfate(VI) ion	sulphate ion	SO_4^{2-}
(fully, tetraoxosulfate(VI) ion)		
sulfate(IV) ion	sulphite ion	SO_3^{2-}
(fully, trioxosulfate(IV) ion)		
sulfur		
(allotropes may be distinguished as [alpha]rhombic and [beta]monoclinic forms of octasulfur, and polysulfur.)		
disulfur dichloride	sulphur monochloride	S_2Cl_2
sulfur dichloride oxide	thionyl chloride	SCl_2O
sulfur dioxide		SO_2
(this exists as discrete molecules at all times, unlike sulfur(VI) oxide)		
sulfur trioxide*		SO_3
(when vaporised, a mixture of polymeric species is present. The name sulfur trioxide indicates the stoichiometry but must not be regarded as conveying structural information. For this reason some prefer the name sulfur(VI) oxide, a name earlier recommended but which poses the problem of treating SO_2 and SO_3 differently.)		

* Composition indefinite or structure complicated: see note 2, Section 5.3.1.
n.c. No change.

Recommended name	Traditional name	Formula
sulfuric(VI) acid (fully, tetraoxosulfuric(VI) acid)	sulphuric acid	H_2SO_4
sulfuric(IV) acid (fully, trioxosulfuric(IV) acid)	sulphurous acid	H_2SO_3
thiocyanate ion		CNS^-
tetrathionate ion		$S_4O_6^{2-}$
thiosulfate ion	thiosulphate ion	$S_2O_3^{2-}$
(discussion of oxidation numbers here raises problems)		
tin(II) ion	stannous ion	Sn^{2+}
tin(IV) ion	stannic ion	Sn^{4+}
titanium(II) ion		Ti^{2+}
titanium(III) ion	titanous ion	Ti^{3+}
titanium(IV) ion	titanic ion	Ti^{4+}
titanium(IV) oxide	titanium dioxide	TiO_2
tungstate(VI) ion*		
(fully, polytetraoxotungstate(VI) ion although the simple WO_4^{2-} ion is found in very alkaline solutions)		
uranate(VI) ion*		
(most uranates contain the heptaoxodiuranate(VI) ion)		
uranyl(VI) ion (also named 'dioxouranium(VI) ion')		UO_2^{2+}
vanadate(IV)* ion	vanadite (hypovanadite)ion	
vanadate(V) ion	orthovanadate ion	VO_3^-
vanadium(II) ion	vanadous ion	V^{2+}
vanadium(III) ion	vanadic ion	V^{3+}
vanadium(V) oxide	vanadium pentoxide	V_2O_5
See also oxovanadium(IV) ion		
zinc ion		Zn^{2+}
zinc carbonate (calamine)	calamine	$ZnCO_3$
zinc silicate (smithsonite)	smithsonite	$ZnSiO_4$
(the two mineral names above are transposed in American usage)		
zincate ion*		

* Composition indefinite or structure complicated: see note 2, Section 5.3.1.
n.c. No change.

5.4   Traditional names for inorganic species

5.4.1   Notes

1 The symbol * after a name in this section indicates that the composition is indefinite or the structure complicated: a full systematic name and structural formula are considered inappropriate for the 16–19 age range.

2 *see* refers the reader to a note at the entry in 5.3.2.

3 n.c. means that no change is recommended.

4 Minerals are named as shown in the examples below, with the systematic name preceding the trivial name of the mineral.

5 In accordance with international agreement, the name **sulphur** is changed to **sulfur** (and compounds similarly). (No change has been suggested to the spelling of phosphorus!)

5.4.2   Traditional names: inorganic

Traditional name		Recommended name
actinide		actinoid
alum		aluminium potassium sulfate(VI)-12-water
	see	5.2.4
aluminate ion		aluminate ion*
aluminium		**n.c. in names of elements, except S which becomes sulfur**
aluminium ion	*see*	aluminium ion
aluminium ion (hydrated)	*see*	hexaaquaaluminium(III) ion
aluminium acetate		basic aluminium ethanoate*
aluminium halides	*see*	aluminium bromide
aluminium hydroxide		hydrated aluminium hydroxide
aluminium trimethyl		trimethylaluminium
ammonia		n.c. (the name azane *might* be adopted in the future)
ammonium alum		aluminium ammonium sulfate(VI)-12-water
ammonium hydroxide		aqueous ammonia
ammonium ion		n.c.
ammoniacal cuprous chloride		ammoniacal copper(I) chloride
ammoniacal silver nitrate		ammoniacal silver nitrate(V)
	see	note on 'silver(I) ion'
anhydrite		calcium sulfate(VI) (anhydrite)
antimonate ion		antimonate(V) ion*
antimonite ion		antimonate(III) ion*
antimony pentoxide		antimony(V) oxide
antimony trichloride		antimony(III) chloride
antimonyl chloride		antimony(III) chloride oxide
antimonyl potassium tartrate		antimony(III) potassium; 2,3-dihydroxybutanedioate oxide
argentous ion	*see*	silver(I) ion
arsenate ion		arsenate(V) ion
arsenic trichloride		n.c.
arsenic pentoxide (arsenic oxide)		arsenic(V) oxide*
arsenic trioxide (arsenious oxide)		arsenic(III) oxide*
arsenite ion		arsenate(III) ion*
arsine		n.c.
atomic hydrogen, oxygen, etc.		monohydrogen etc.
azide ion		n.c.
barium ion		n.c.
bauxite		hydrated aluminium oxide (bauxite)

(other minerals are named similarly. See Section 5.4.1 above. Very few minerals, of course, are pure.)

---

*   Composition indefinite or structure complicated: see note 2, Section 5.3.1.
n.c. No change.

Traditional name	Recommended name
beryllium acetate(basic)	basic beryllium ethanoate
bicarbonate, bisulphate, etc.	hydrogencarbonate, hydrogensulfate(VI), etc.
binoxalate ion	hydrogenethanedioate ion
bismuth ion	bismuth(III) ion
bismuth oxychloride	bismuth(III) chloride oxide
	(other basic salts are named similarly)
bismuth trichloride	bismuth(III) chloride
bismuthate ion	bismuthate(V) ion*
bismuthyl chloride	bismuth(III) chloride oxide
(bismuth oxychloride)	
bleaching powder	n.c.*
borax	*see* disodium tetraborate(III)-10-water
boric acid	*see* boric acid*
boric oxide	boron(III) oxide*
borohydride ion	tetrahydridoborate(III) ion
boron trifluoride	n.c.
bromate ion	*see* bromate(V) ion
bromic acid	*see* bromic(V) acid
bromine trifluoride	n.c.
buckminsterfullerene	carbon (fullerene)
cadmium ion	n.c.
calamine	*see* zinc carbonate (calamine)
calcite	calcium carbonate (calcite)
calcium acetylide	calcium dicarbide or diethynediide (*see* Section 5.2.1)
calcium ion	n.c.
calcium carbide	calcium dicarbide or diethynediide (*see* Section 5.2.1)
calcium cyanamide	n.c.
calcium stearate	calcium octadecanoate
calomel	dimercury(I) chloride
	but see dimercury(I) ion
carbamate ion	n.c.
carbide ion	*see* carbide ion
carbon dioxide	n.c.
carbon disulphide	carbon disulfide
carbon monoxide	n.c.
(other monoxides are, according to IUPAC Rules, called simply 'oxide', but see nitrogen monoxide for	
recommendation)	
carbon tetrachloride	*see* tetrachloromethane and Section 6.3.2
carbonate ion	n.c.
Caro's acid	peroxosulfuric(VI) acid
cerate ion	cerate(IV) ion*
ceric ion	cerium(IV) ion
cerous ion	cerium(III) ion
cerussite	lead(II) carbonate (cerussite)
chalcopyrite	copper(II) iron(II) disulfide (chalcopyrite)
charcoal	carbon(charcoal)
chloramine	n.c.
chlorate ion	*see* chlorate(V) ion
chloric acid	*see* chloric(V) acid
chloride ion	n.c.
chlorine dioxide	n.c.
chlorine monoxide	dichlorine oxide
chlorite ion	*see* chlorate(III) ion
chlorosulphonic acid	chlorosulfonic acid
chlorous acid	*see* chloric(III) acid

*   Composition indefinite or structure complicated: see note 2, Section 5.3.1.
n.c. No change.

Traditional name		Recommended name
chromate ion	*see*	chromate(VI) ion
chrome alum		chromium(III) potassium sulfate-12-water
chromic acid	*see*	chromic(VI) acid
chromic ion		chromium(III) ion
chromite ion		chromate(III) ion*
	but see	dichromium(III) copper(II) oxide
chromium sesquioxide		chromium(III) oxide
chromium trioxide		chromium(VI) oxide
chromous ion		chromium(II) ion
chromyl chloride		chromium(VI) dichloride dioxide
cobalt ion (cobaltous ion)		cobalt(II) ion
cobalti-cobaltous oxide		cobalt(II) dicobalt(III) oxide
cobaltic acetylacetonate		tris(pentane-2,4-dionato)cobalt(III)
cobalticyanide ion		hexacyanocobaltate(III) ion
cobaltinitrite ion		hexanitrocobaltate(III) ion
copper pyrites		copper(II) iron(II) disulfide (chalcopyrite)
cryolite		sodium hexafluoroaluminate(III) (cryolite)
cuprammonium ion	*see*	tetraamminecopper(II) ion
cupric ion		copper(II) ion
cupric ion (hydrated)	*see*	hexaaquaaluminium ion
cupric sulphate	*see*	copper(II) sulfate(VI)
cuprichloride ion		tetrachlorocuprate(II) ion
cuprochloride ion		trichlorocuprate(I) ion
cuprous acetylide		dicopper(I) ethynediide
cuprous chloride (ammoniacal)		diamminecopper(I) chloride
cuprous ion		copper(I) ion
cuprous potassium cyanide		potassium tetracyanocuprate(I)
cyanate ion		n.c.
cyanide ion		n.c.
cyanogen		n.c.
diamond		carbon(diamond)
dichromate ion	*see*	dichromate(VI) ion
diphosphine		diphosphane
dolomite		calcium magnesium biscarbonate (dolomite)
ferric chloride		iron(III) chloride
ferric ion		iron(III) ion
ferricyanide ion		hexacyanoferrate(III) ion
ferrocyanide ion		hexacyanoferrate(II) ion
ferrosoferric oxide		iron(II) diiron(III) oxide
ferrous ion		iron(II) ion
fluoride ion		n.c.
fluorine monoxide		oxygen difluoride
fluorosilicate ion		hexafluorosilicate(IV) ion
graphite		carbon (graphite)
gypsum		calcium sulfate(VI)-2-water (gypsum)
haematite		iron(III) oxide (haematite)
hydrazine		n.c. (*possibly* diazane in the future)
hydrazoic acid		n.c.
hydrogen ion		n.c.
	but see	oxonium ion
hydrogen fluoride ion		hydrogendifluoride ion
hydrogen peroxide		n.c.
hydronium ion	*see*	oxonium ion

* Composition indefinite or structure complicated: see note 2, Section 5.3.1.
n.c. No change.

Traditional name		Recommended name
hydrosulphide ion		hydrogensulfide ion
hydroxyl group		n.c.
hydroxyl ion		hydroxide ion
hydroxylamine		n.c.
hypobromite ion	*see*	bromate(I) ion
hypobromous acid	*see*	bromic(I) acid
hypochlorite ion	*see*	chlorate(I) ion
hypochlorous acid	*see*	chloric(I) acid
hypophosphite ion		phosphinate ion
hyposulphite ion		sulfinate ion
inert gases		noble gases
iodate ion	*see*	iodate(V) ion
iodic acid	*see*	iodic(V) acid
iodide ion		n.c.
iodine monochloride		n.c.
(the IUPAC name is iodine chloride but the 'mono' is retained for clarity)		
iodine pentoxide		iodine(V) oxide*
iodine trichloride		diiodine hexachloride
iodonium ion		iodine(I) ion
iron pentacarbonyl		pentacarbonyliron(0)
iron pyrites		iron(II) disulfide(pyrites)
lanthanide		lanthanoid
lead acetate		lead(II) ethanoate
lead dioxide		lead(IV) oxide
lead ion		lead(II) ion
lead monoxide		lead(II) oxide
lead tetraacetate		lead(IV) ethanoate
lead tetraethyl		tetraethyllead(IV)
lithium aluminium hydride		lithium tetrahydridoaluminate(III)
magnesium ion		n.c.
magnetite		iron(II) diiron(III) oxide(magnetite)
malachite		copper(II) carbonate dihydroxide (malachite)
manganate ion	*see*	manganate(VI) ion
manganese alums	*as*	caesium manganese(III) sulfate(VI)-12-water, etc.
manganese carbonate		manganese(II) carbonate
(both basic and true carbonates are known)		
manganese dioxide		manganese(IV) oxide
manganese heptoxide		manganese(VII) oxide
manganic ion		manganese(III) ion
mangano-manganic oxide		manganese(II) dimanganese(III) oxide
manganous ion		manganese(II) ion
mercuric ion		mercury(II) ion
mercuriiodide ion		tetraiodomercurate(II) ion
mercurous ion	*see*	dimercury(I) ion
metabisulphite ion	*see*	disulfate(IV) ion
metaboric acid		polydioxoboric(III) acid
	but see	boric acid*
metaphosphate		polytrioxophosphate(V)*
metavanadate		polytrioxovanadate(V)*
molybdate ion		molybdate(VI) ion
nickel carbonyl		tetracarbonylnickel(0)
nickel-dimethylglyoxime		bis(butanedione dioximato)nickel(II)

*   Composition indefinite or structure complicated: see note 2, Section 5.3.1.
n.c. No change.

Traditional name		Recommmended name
nickel ion (nickelous ion)		nickel(II) ion
nickelocyanide ion		tetracyanonickelate(II) ion
nitrate ion	*see*	nitrate(V) ion
nitric acid	*see*	nitric(V) acid
nitric oxide	*see*	nitrogen monoxide
nitride ion		n.c.
nitrite ion	*see*	nitrate(III) ion
nitrogen dioxide (nitrogen peroxide)	*see*	nitrogen dioxide
nitronium ion		nitryl cation
nitroprusside ion		pentacyanonitrosylferrate(II) ion
nitrosyl ion		nitrosyl cation
nitrous acid	*see*	nitric(III) acid
nitrous oxide		dinitrogen oxide
oleum (a solution of SO_3 in H_2SO_4)		n.c.
orthoboric acid		trioxoboric acid
	but see	boric acid*
orthoperiodic acid		hexaoxoiodic(VII) acid
orthophosphate ion	*see*	phosphate(V) ion
orthoplumbate ion		plumbate(IV) ion
ozone	*see*	trioxygen
per-acids (containing the –O–O– group)		peroxoacids
perborate ion	*see*	peroxoborate(III) ion
perchlorate ion	*see*	chlorate(VII) ion
perdisulphuric acid		peroxodisulfuric(VI) acid
periodate ion	*see*	iodate(VII) ion
permanganate ion	*see*	manganate(VII) ion
permonosulphuric acid		peroxosulfuric(VI) acid
phosphate ion	*see*	phosphate(V) ion
phosphine		n.c.
phosphite ion		phosphonate ion
phosphonium ion		n.c.
phosphoric acid	*see*	phosphoric(V) acid
phosphorous acid		phosphonic acid
	see	phosphonic acid and phosphorus(III) acid
phosphorus	*see*	phosphorus, for allotropes
phosphorus oxyhalides		as phosphorus trichloride oxide
phosphorus pentahalides		n.c.
	but see	phosphorus(V) chloride
phosphorus pentoxide	*see*	phosphorus(V) oxide
phosphorus trihalides		n.c.
phosphorus trioxide		phosphorus(III) oxide
phosphoryl chloride		phosphorus trichloride oxide
plaster of Paris		calcium sulfate(VI)-$\frac{1}{2}$-water
plumbane		n.c.
plumbate ion		plumbate(IV) ion
plumbic compounds		lead(IV) compounds
plumbichloride ion		hexachloroplumbate(IV) ion
plumbite ion		plumbate(II) ion
plumbous ion		lead(II) ion
potassium antimonyl tartrate		antimony(III) potassium 2,3-dihydroxybutanedioate oxide
potassium ion		n.c.
pyrites		iron(II) disulfide (pyrites)
pyrophosphate ion		heptaoxodiphosphate(V) ion

---

*   Composition indefinite or structure complicated: see note 2, Section 5.3.1.
n.c. No change.

Traditional name		Recommmended name
quicklime		calcium oxide
red lead	*see*	dilead(II) lead(IV) oxide
silane (and substituted silanes)		n.c.
silica	*see*	silicon(IV) oxide
silicate ion		n.c.*
silicofluoride ion		hexafluorosilicate(IV) ion
silicon dioxide		silicon(IV) oxide*
silicon tetrachloride		n.c.
silver ion	*see*	silver(I) ion
slaked lime		calcium hydroxide
sodalime (as reagent)		n.c.*
sodium ion		n.c.
stannane		n.c
stannate ion		stannate(IV) ion
stannic compounds		tin(IV) compounds
stannichloride ion		hexachlorostannate(IV) ion
stannite ion		stannate(II) ion*
stannous ion		tin(II) ion
stibine		n.c.
strontium ion		n.c.
sulphamic acid		aminosulfonic acid
sulphate ion	*see*	sulfate(VI) ion
sulphite ion	*see*	sulfate(IV) ion
sulphur	*see*	sulfur, for allotropes
sulphur dioxide		sulfur dioxide
sulphur monochloride		disulfur dichloride
sulphur trioxide	*see*	sulfur trioxide*
sulphuric acid	*see*	sulfuric(VI) acid
sulphurous acid	*see*	sulfuric(IV) acid
sulphuryl chloride		sulfur dichloride dioxide
tetrathionate ion		n.c.
thioantimonate ion		tetrathioantimonate(V) ion
thioantimonite ion		trithioantimonate(III) ion
thioarsenate ion		tetrathioarsenate(V) ion
thioarsenite ion		trithioarsenate(III) ion
thiocyanate ion		n.c.
thionyl chloride		sulfur dichloride oxide
thiostannate ion		trithiostannate(IV) ion
	or	tetrathiostannate(IV) ion, as appropriate
thiosulphate ion	*see*	thiosulfate ion
tin dioxide		tin(IV) oxide
titanic compounds		titanium(IV) compounds
titanium dichloride		titanium(II) chloride
titanium dioxide		titanium(IV) oxide
titanous compounds		titanium(III) compounds
tungstate ion	*see*	tungstate(VI) ion*
uranate ion	*see*	uranate(VI) ion*
uranyl ion (UO$_2^{2+}$)	*see*	uranyl(VI) ion
vanadate ion		vanadate(V) ion
vanadic ion		vanadium(III) ion
vanadite (hypovanadite) ion		vanadate(IV) ion*

* Composition indefinite or structure complicated: see note 2, Section 5.3.1.
n.c. No change.

Traditional name	Recommmended name
vanadium pentoxide	vanadium(v) oxide
vanadous ion	vanadium(II) ion
vanadyl sulphate ($VOSO_4$)	oxovanadium(IV) sulfate(VI)
white lead	lead carbonate hydroxide
zincate ion	zincate ion*
zinc ion	n.c.
zinc uranyl acetate	dioxouranium(VI) zinc ethanoate*

---

*   Composition indefinite or structure complicated: see note 2, Section 5.3.1.
n.c. No change.

6 CHEMICAL NOMENCLATURE: ORGANIC

6.1 General introduction

This section describes the systems for naming organic compounds, designed to give unambiguous systematic names as far as possible.

Names can be *trivial* or *systematic*. Trivial names such as 'starch' or 'litmus' serve to identify what is in a bottle. Systematic names not only identify what is in the bottle but also give more information about the composition and molecular structure of the substance. Systematic names are usually longer or more complicated than trivial names, because they carry much more information: the trivial name 'isooctane' is shorter than '2,2,4-trimethylpentane' but also tells us less.

The systematic name and the formula of a compound are closely related. If the detailed formula of a compound is important and meaningful to the student we should use the systematic name, but temper the complexity of the name to the needs of the student.

6.2 Rules for naming organic compounds

6.2.1 Substitutive nomenclature

Compounds are named as though they are hydrocarbons (as chains or homocyclic rings) or as heterocyclic rings, and then any atoms or groups of atoms that are not hydrogen atoms are considered to have been substituted for the hydrogen atoms.

For example, CH_3CH_2Cl can be considered to be ethane with one chlorine atom substituting for a hydrogen atom, so its name is chloroethane.

6.2.2 Order of priority of suffixes and prefixes

The name of the root hydrocarbon (or heterocyclic compound) has prefixes and/or suffixes added to indicate the atoms or groups of atoms that have been substituted for hydrogen atoms. If it can, a suffix should be used rather than the corresponding prefix. If another (different) suffix takes priority the prefix is used.

For example, the carbonyl function of a ketone is usually described by a suffix, e.g. $CH_3CH_2COCH_2CH_3$ is pentan-3-one; but if there is a carboxylic acid function present, its suffix takes priority, so that the carbonyl group in $CH_3CH_2COCH_2COOH$ is described by a prefix: 3-oxopentanoic acid.

As many prefixes as are necessary can be used, but *only one suffix may be used* in any one compound. (The syllables 'an' (or 'ane'), 'en' (or 'ene') and 'yn' (or 'yne') are considered to be part of the root and not a suffix.)

Where there is a choice of suffixes, the one nearest the top of the list below is used in preference. The remaining groups on the hydrocarbon are then described by prefixes, which are arranged alphabetically if different groups are present.

Multiplying prefixes are disregarded in determining the alphabetical order to use, e.g. CH_2ClCBr_2COOH is dibromochloropropanoic acid (i.e. the di- is ignored in placing bromo- in front of chloro- alphabetically). Other multiplying prefixes are: tri-, tetra-, penta-, hexa-, hepta-, octa-, etc. (these follow the familiar Greek pattern).

The rest of this sub-section gives some examples. Where a carbon atom is bracketed, that atom is taken to be part of the hydrocarbon that forms the root of the name, and the suffix must be used.

Formula of group	Name as prefix	Name as suffix	Example(s)
$\overset{\mid}{\underset{\mid}{-N-}}^{+}$	(none)	-ammonium	$(CH_3)_3NH^+Br^-$ trimethylammonium bromide
—COOH	carboxy-	-carboxylic acid	benzene-1,2-dicarboxylic acid 3-carboxyphenylammonium bromide
$\overset{\mid}{\underset{OH}{-(C)=O}}$	(none)	-oic acid	CH_3CH_2COOH propanoic acid
—COO⁻	(none)	-carboxylate (ion)	$NH_2C_6H_4COO^-Na^+$ sodium aminobenzenecarboxylate
$\overset{\mid}{\underset{O^-}{-(C)=O}}$	(none)	-oate (ion)	$CH_3COO^-K^+$ potassium ethanoate
—COOR	alkoxycarbonyl-	alkyl (hydrocarbon)carboxylate	$C_2H_5C_6H_4COOCH_3$ methyl ethylbenzenecarboxylate
$\overset{\mid}{\underset{OR}{-(C)=O}}$	(none)	alkyl (hydrocarbon)oate	$CH_3CH_2CH_2COOCH_2CH_3$ ethyl butanoate
—COHal	halogenocarbonyl-	-carbonyl halide	2-(chlorocarbonyl) benzenecarboxylic acid
$\overset{\mid}{\underset{OHal}{-(C)=O}}$	(none)	-oyl halide	CH_3CH_2COBr propanoyl bromide

Formula of group	Name as prefix	Name as suffix	Example(s)
—$CONH_2$	carbamoyl-	-carboxamide	2-carbamoylbenzene-carboxylic acid benzene-1,2-dicarboxamide
—(C)=O | NH_2	(none)	-amide	$CH_3CH_2CONH_2$ propanamide
—CN	cyano-	-carbonitrile	2-cyanobenzenecarboxylic acid benzene-1,2-dicarbonitrile
—(C)≡N	(none)	-nitrile	CH_3CH_2CN propanenitrile
—CHO	methanoyl- (the traditional name formyl- is sometimes used)	-carbaldehyde	2-methanoylbenzene-carboxylic acid benzene-1,2-dicarbaldehyde
—(C)=O | H	oxo-	-al	CH_2CH_2COOH | CHO 4-oxobutanoic acid $CH_3CH_2CH_2CHO$ butanal

Formula of group	Name as prefix	Name as suffix	Example(s)
—(C)=O	oxo-	-one	CH_3COCH_3 propanone
			$CH_3COCOOH$ 2-oxopropanoic acid
—OH	hydroxy-	-ol	CH_3CH_2OH ethanol
			2- hydroxybenzene-carboxylic acid
—SH	sulfanyl-	-thiol	CH_3CH_2SH ethanethiol
			$HS–CH_2COOH$ sulfanylethanoic acid
—NH_2	amino-	-amine	$CH_3CH_2NH_2$ ethylamine (but see Section 6.2.4)

6.2.3   Numbering of locants

When there is a choice of positions, it is necessary to indicate precisely where a functional group is in a chain. To do this, the carbon atoms in the parent hydrocarbon (the root) are numbered and the appropriate number (which is called the *locant*) is put before the prefix or suffix. For example:

$$\overset{1}{C}H_3\overset{2}{C}HCl\overset{3}{C}H_3 \qquad \text{2-chloropropane.}$$

The numbering system is arranged so that the group described is given the lowest possible number, for example:

$$\overset{1}{C}H_3\overset{2}{C}H_2\overset{3}{C}H(OH)\overset{4}{C}H_3 \qquad \text{butan-3-ol, if numbering is from the left}$$

or

$$\overset{4}{C}H_3\overset{3}{C}H_2\overset{2}{C}H(OH)\overset{1}{C}H_3 \qquad \text{butan-2-ol, if numbering is from the right.}$$

Butan-2-ol is the preferred name as the locant is lower.

In some cases the root hydrocarbon chain must be numbered from the carbon atom to which a functional group is bonded. These occur when a suffix is used that necessitates the inclusion of the carbon atom to which a functional group is bonded as part of the root.

For example, the numbering of the carbon atoms in $CH_3CHBrCH_2COOH$ must be from the carboxylic acid group and its name is 3-bromobutanoic acid rather than 2-bromobutanoic acid.

Where more than one locant is required, the chain (or ring) is numbered so that the preferred name has the lower number on the first instance when a difference would occur.

For example, $CH_3CH_2CHBrCHBrCH_2CH_2CH_2CHBrCH_3$ could be 2,7,8-tribromodecane or 3,4,9-tribromodecane. The former is preferred because 2 is lower than 3. Note that it is not the total of the locants that is used:

$2 + 7 + 8 = 17$, while $3 + 4 + 9 = 16$

When a double bond is present the lower locant is used, referring to the carbon atom nearer the end of the hydrocarbon chain from which numbering began, for example:

$CH_3CH=CHCH_2CH_3$ is pent-2-ene, not pent-3-ene

6.2.4   Naming of amines

The naming of amines differs from that of most other compounds in that they are not derived from a parent hydrocarbon which is then considered to have been substituted, but from the combination of two radicals, 'alkyl' and 'amine'. This gives the names 'methylamine', 'ethylamine', etc.; and their relationship to their conjugate acids methylammonium, ethylammonium, etc., is then clear. Similarly $C_6H_5NH_2$ is named phenylamine and $C_6H_5NH_3^+$ phenylammonium. (The names aniline and anilinium are not recommended.)

The naming of secondary and tertiary amines and their salts, and quaternary ammonium salts, is similar:

Amine	Name	Salt	Name
CH_3NH_2	methylamine	$CH_3NH_3^+$	methylammonium
$(CH_3)_2NH$	dimethylamine	$(CH_3)_2NH_2^+$	dimethylammonium
$(CH_3)_3N$	trimethylamine	$(CH_3)_3NH^+$	trimethylammonium
		$(CH_3)_4N^+$	tetramethylammonium

It has been suggested that the parent hydrocarbon should be given more prominence and that ethylamine should be named 'ethanamine' (and so on). Although this does make sense for primary amines, it does not work for secondary (etc.) compounds. Our recommendation is that at 16–19 level it should not be used. The use of 'nitrilo-' for ≡N is likely to cause 16–19 students to confuse ≡N with –C≡N.

The group $–NH_2$ is named as a prefix only when the molecule includes a group of higher priority which takes the suffix position, for example:

is 4-aminobenzenecarboxylic acid.

When an amine group is not bonded to the first carbon atom of an alkyl chain, or when the molecule contains more than one amine group, a substitutive name such as propane-2-amine or hexane-1,6-diamine (corresponding acid hexane-1,6-diammonium) may be used. The use of propan-2-ylamine for the amine

$$CH_3CHCH_3$$
$$|$$
$$NH_2$$

is also possible, and is preferred to propan-2-amine.

It has been suggested that compounds derived from ammonia have the suffix '-azane' and those derived from hydrogen sulfide have the suffix '-sulfane'. For example, CH_3NH_2 would be methylazane and CH_3SH would be methylsulfane. These names are based on the premise that the chemistry of nitrogen or sulfur is more important than that of the organic chains bonded to them. Our recommendation is that until the name azane replaces ammonia and sulfane replaces hydrogen sulfide (this has not yet happened), names based on them should not be used in chemistry at the 16–19 level.

6.2.5   Naming of aromatic compounds

The carbon atoms in a benzene ring are numbered as for aliphatic compounds, but the numbering starts at the atom to which the principal group is bonded, for example:

COOH

OH

is called 2-hydroxybenzenecarboxylic acid.

The naming of aromatic compounds is further complicated by the fact that the suffixes -al, -one, -oic acid, and those for carboxylic acid derivatives, all require the inclusion of the carbon atom of the group in the naming of the root name. Taking C_6H_5CHO as an example, there is no root name for the hydrocarbon $C_6H_5CH_3$; and no compound conforms to the name benzenal. The name benzaldehyde is used for this compound, and C_6H_5COOH is called benzoic acid (strictly it should be called benzenecarboxylic acid, and while this term is used for its derivatives the simpler name, benzoic acid, tends to be used for the simple acid). When there is more than one aldehydic group the suffix -carbaldehyde is appropriate, for example:

CHO

CHO   is benzene-1,2-dicarbaldehyde.

Although in schools numbers are used as locants for aromatic compounds, in some texts where two groups are bonded to an aromatic ring it is possible that the bonding positions on the ring will be described by the prefixes *ortho-*, *meta-*, or *para-* (often abbreviated to *o-*, *m-*, and *p-*) rather than (numerical) locants. These prefixes indicate that the groups are bonded in the 1 and 2, 1 and 3, or 1 and 4 positions respectively, for example:

Br

Br

Cl

Cl

NO$_2$

NO$_2$

o-dibromobenzene
1,2-dibromobenzene

m-dichlorobenzene
1,3-dichlorobenzene

p-dinitrobenzene
1,4-dinitrobenzene

The prefixes *ortho- meta-* and *para-* are of use in cases only where there are two substituent groups on a benzene ring.

The name phenol and the prefix phenyl- do not seem to have any connection with benzene. They are derived from the name 'phene', which was once proposed to replace the name benzene. This was unsuccessful; however some of the names based on it have remained. For instance, monohydroxy compounds of benzene are still called phenols, though polyhydroxy compounds are given systematic names, for example:

Cl

OH

is named 2-chlorophenol, while

OH

OH

is benzene-1,3-diol

The five- and six-membered heterocyclic ring compounds thiophene and pyridine are other examples of compounds whose non-systematic names have remained:

S

N

thiophene   pyridine

There are not six delocalized electrons in the thiophene molecule so the circle cannot be used: neither of these compounds is likely to be met in 16–19 chemistry.

The prefix *phenyl-* is retained for the C_6H_5- group.

Hydrocarbons with an alkyl side chain bonded to a benzene ring are usually named as alkylbenzenes. When the side chain contains a functional group, it is possible to name the compound as either a benzene derivative or as a phenyl substituted aliphatic compound. The name given in schools is usually chosen to focus on the part of the structure that is most likely to be involved in reactions, for example:

would be called methylbenzene rather than phenylmethane, whereas

would be called phenylethene rather than ethenylbenzene.

As a result, for some compounds, more than one name can be correctly constructed and each adequately describes the structure. The preferred name should be used for the 16–19 age group. (This does not mean that the alternative names are incorrect.)

6.2.6   Use of multiplying prefixes

There is often more than one way of adding a multiplying prefix, e.g. bi-, di-, bis-. Each of these has a different meaning. (Others are tri-, tris-; and tetra-, tetrakis-).

Di- is used to denote the attachment of two identical atoms or groups in a compound, e.g. dinitrobenzene:

This example is named 1,3-dinitrobenzene.

Bis- is used when the expression to be multiplied already has a multiplying prefix, e.g. bis-1,3-(dichloromethyl)benzene:

Bi- is used to indicate the linking together of two groups which together form the root of the structure, e.g.

is biphenyl-4,4$'$-dicarboxylic acid. (The prime $'$ on one locant is used to show that the substituted group is in the 4 position on a different ring.)

6.2.7   Use of elemental symbols as prefixes

In some cases it is not appropriate to give a numerical locant that identifies where a group has been substituted – usually when the group is bonded to a hetero atom. In such cases use of the symbol of the element to which the group is bonded can be used. For instance, the name phenylethanamide does not permit unambiguous location of the phenyl group, whereas N-phenylethanamide does:

C-phenylethanamide
(2-phenylethanamide would be preferred
unless the important point is a comparison
of the two.)

N-phenylethanamide

6.2.8   Trivial names

Although systematic nomenclature is designed to make naming and drawing structures easy, it is not always most appropriate to use it. This is especially the case where complex structures are involved, whose systematic names are too complicated for students to work out, or excessively long. In such cases, it is quite acceptable to use a trivial name. Keep in mind that it is usually the chemistry of such compounds that is being studied, and not the naming system in itself. If the molecular structure is important to the student then the systematic name should be used; if not, then a trivial name can be used (e.g. methyl orange).

Using trivial names or abbreviations can be justified when *sequences* of molecules are more important than the structures of the molecules themselves. An example is the sequence of amino-acid residues in proteins. The abbreviations Arg, Lys, Tyr, Val, etc. are acceptable in this case. When it is the *structures* of these substances (amino-acid residues) that are being studied, systematic names would normally be used.

Other examples of biochemical significance include the following.

Trivial name	Systematic name
pyruvic acid	2-oxopropanoic acid
glycerol	propane-1,2,3-triol (or, more simply, propanetriol, since the presence of two –OH groups on one carbon atom is *usually* unstable)
triglyceride	tri(acyloxy)propane
aniline hydrochloride	phenylammonium chloride
malonate ion	$CH_2(COO^-)_2$ propanedioate ion

6.2.9   Polymers

Most polymers are named according to one of two systems. Most *addition* polymers are named according to the monomer (the starting material, or source) from which they were formed, while most *condensation* polymers are described by the types of linkages involved in their structures.

The source-based naming of addition polymers leads to poly(alkene) descriptions, e.g. poly(ethene), poly(phenylethene). These names are preferred at the 16–19 age level.

Examples of some polymers and their names are given opposite.

Structure	Source-based name	Commercial name	Common abbreviation
$\left[\!\!-CH_2\!-\!CH_2\!-\!\right]_n$	poly(ethene)	polythene	pe
$\left[\!\!-CH_2\!-\!\underset{\displaystyle CH_3}{\overset{\displaystyle \vert}{CH}}\!-\!\right]_n$	poly(propene)	polypropylene	pp
$\left[\!\!-CH_2\!-\!\underset{\displaystyle C_6H_5}{\overset{\displaystyle \vert}{CH_2}}\!-\!\right]_n$	poly(phenylethene)	polystyrene	ps
$\left[\!\!-CH_2\!-\!\underset{\displaystyle Cl}{\overset{\displaystyle \vert}{CH_2}}\!-\!\right]_n$	poly(chloroethene)	polyvinyl chloride	pvc
$\left[\!\!-CF_2\!-\!CF_2\!-\!\right]_n$	poly(tetrafluoroethene)	polytetrafluoroethylene	ptfe
$\left[\!\!-CH_2\!-\!\underset{\displaystyle OCOCH_3}{\overset{\displaystyle \vert}{CH}}\!-\!\right]_n$	poly(ethanoyloxyethene)	polyvinyl acetate	pva
$\left[\!\!-CH_2\!-\!\underset{\displaystyle COOCH_3}{\overset{\displaystyle \vert}{\underset{\vert}{C}}}\overset{\displaystyle CH_3}{}\!-\!\right]_n$	poly(methyl 2-methylpropenoate)	polymethyl methacrylate; Perspex; acrylic	pmma

Using an alternative (but less preferable) system for naming these polymers, poly(tetrafluoroethene) is called poly(difluoromethylene). This system is structure-based, and in this case the smallest repeating entity is the difluoromethylene group, $-CF_2-$.

The source-based nomenclature is preferred at 16–19 level because it places greater emphasis on the polymerisation process rather than on the final product: if students know how addition polymerisation takes place they can work out the polymer structures for themselves.

Most condensation polymers are identified by the linkages formed as the polymers formed. It would be extremely difficult to compose meaningful systematic names for most condensation polymers, and they are often described by simple block diagrams such as:

... –X–O–X–O–X–O– ...

or, if the bonding is to be illustrated, as, for example:

... –NHCO–☐–CONH–X–NHCO–☐–CONH–X–NHCO–☐–CONH–X–NHCO–...

The latter structure is that of a polyamide such as Nylon-6,6.

The name Nylon-6 indicates one starting material, and six carbon atoms in each monomer molecule. In order to achieve the $-CONH-$ linkage (the same as that seen in proteins), the monomer must have had an acid group at one end ($-COOH$), and an amino at the other ($-NH_2$).

The name Nylon-6,6 indicates two starting materials, each with six carbon atoms in its molecule: one a diamine (hexane-1,6-diamine) and one a diacid (hexanedioic acid). Similarly Nylon-6,10 has the same amine containing six carbon atoms and a diacid with ten carbon atoms (decanedioic acid).

The other common linking seen in condensation polymers is that of polyesters. Terylene is one such polymer, and it has the structure

$$-\left(-OCH_2-CH_2-O-CO-C_6H_4-CO-\right)_n$$

It, too, can be described by block diagrams – including or excluding the precise nature of the ester linkages, for example:

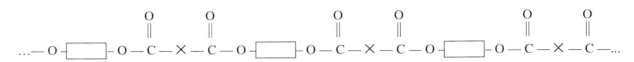

Note that proprietary names registered as trademarks should be spelt with a capital letter and not used as a generic name. Nylon, Perspex and Terylene are examples of such names.

Source-based and, even more, structure-based names for condensation polymers are probably too complex to be used, although 'poly(ethylene terephthalate)' (trivial name) does show where the name Terylene came from. The systematic name 'poly(ethenediyl 1,4-benzenedicarboxylate)' does not!

6.3   Systematic names for organic species

6.3.1   Notes

1 The 'recommended name' given here is that recommended for general use and for labelling substances and is a systematic name. Other names given in parentheses are more detailed systematic names appropriate to advanced study of structures or are suitable in some particular context which is stated. Hyphens are not recommended by IUPAC to separate double 'a', etc. (e.g. in hexaaqua) but they may be used if desired for clarity.

2 Multiplying prefixes (e.g. di-. tri-, tetra- hexa-) have been disregarded in arranging the names in alphabetical order

6.3.2   Recommended names: organic

Recommended name	Traditional name(s)
acetals (generic name)	acetals; *gem*-dialkoxyalkanes
acyl	acyl
adenine	adenine
adenosine	adenosine
alcohols (generic name)	alcohols
aldehydes (generic name)	aldehydes
aliphatic	aliphatic
alkanes (generic name)	paraffins
alkanoic acids (generic name)	fatty acids; carboxylic acids

(some have double bonds, e.g. oleic acid, so alkanoic, although more useful than the alternatives, is still rather loose)

alkenes (generic name)	olefins
alkyl	alkyl
alkylmagnesium halides	magnesium alkyl halides (Grignard reagents)
alkynes (generic name)	acetylenes
amines (generic name)	amines
amino acids (generic name)	amino acids

(although these compounds exist as zwitterions it is usually more convenient to name them as amino acids. Trivial names such as glycine, alanine, etc., and their approved abbreviations such as 'gly' and 'ala' are likely to be used in biochemical contexts.)

2-aminobenzenecarboxylic acid	anthranilic acid
4-aminobenzenecarboxylic acid	*p*-aminobenzoic acid
4-aminobenzenesulfonamide	sulphanilamide
4-aminobenzenesulfonic acid	sulphanilic acid
aminobutanedioic acid	aspartic acid
aminoethanoic acid	glycine; aminoacetic acid
2-aminoethanol	ethanolamine
2-aminopentanedioic acid	glutamic acid
2-aminophenol (etc.)	*o*-aminophenol (etc.)
2-aminopropanoic acid	alanine
anthracene	anthracene
anthracene-9,10-dione	9,10-anthraquinone
arenes (generic name)	aromatic hydrocarbons
aromatic (generic term)	aromatic
aryl	aryl

benzene	benzene
benzenecarbaldehyde	benzaldehyde
benzenecarbaldehyde oxime	benzaldoxime
benzenecarbonitrile	benzonitrile
benzenecarbonyl chloride	benzoyl chloride
di(benzenecarbonyl) peroxide	benzoyl peroxide
benzenecarboxamide	benzamide
benzenecarboxylic acid	benzoic acid
benzene-1,4-diamine	*p*-phenylenediamine
benzene-1,4-diammonium chloride	*p*-phenylenediamine dihydrochloride

(the monohydrochloride is 4-aminophenylammonium chloride)

Recommended name	Traditional name(s)
benzenediazonium ion	benzenediazonium ion; phenyldiazonium ion
benzene-1,2-dicarboxamide	phthalamide
benzene-1,2-dicarboximide	phthalimide
benzene-1,2-dicarboxylic acid	phthalic acid
benzene-1,3-dicarboxylic acid	isophthalic acid
benzene-1,4-dicarboxylic acid	terephthalic acid
benzene-1,2-dicarboxylic anhydride	phthalic anhydride
benzene-1,2-diol	catechol
benzene-1,3-diol	resorcinol
benzene-1,4-diol	hydroquinone; quinol
benzeneperoxocarboxylic acid	perbenzoic acid
benzenesulfonic acid	benzenesulphonic acid
benzene-1,2,3-triol	pyrogallic acid; pyrogallol
benzene-1,3,5-triol	phloroglucinol
biphenyl-4,4'-diamine	benzidine
bromobenzene	bromobenzene
N-bromobutanedioic imide	*N*-bromosuccinimide
N-bromoethanamide	*N*-bromoacetamide
bromoethane	ethyl bromide
1,1-dibromoethane	ethylidene dibromide
1 2-dibromoethane	ethylene dibromide
1,1,2,2-tetrabromoethane	acetylene tetrabromide
tribromomethane	bromoform
buta-1,3-diene	butadiene
butanal	butyraldehyde
butane	*n*-butane
butanedial	succinaldehyde
butanedioic acid	succinic acid
butanedione	biacetyl
butanedione dioxime	dimethylglyoxime
butanoic acid	butyric acid
butan-1-ol	*n*-butyl alcohol
butan-2-ol	*sec*-butyl alcohol
butanone	methyl ethyl ketone
butan-2-yl	*sec*-butyl
trans-but-2-enal	crotonaldehyde
but-1-ene	butylene
but-2-ene	butylene
cis-butenedioic acid	maleic acid
trans-butenedioic acid	fumaric acid
cis-butenedioic anhydride	maleic anhydride
trans-but-2-enoic acid	crotonic acid
butyl	*n*-butyl

Recommended name	Traditional name(s)
calcium ethynediide } depending *or* calcium dicarbide } on context	{ calcium carbide calcium acetylide
carbamate ion	carbamate ion
carbamic acid	carbamic acid
carbamide *or* urea	urea
carbonyl dichloride	carbonyl chloride; phosgene
carboxylic acids (generic term)	carboxylic acids
1,2bis[bis (carboxymethyl)amino]ethane	ethylenediaminetetraacetic acid

(this compound is commonly referred to as 'edta'. It loses protons to become a ligand which also is known as 'edta'. The acid is therefore referred to for clarity as H_4edta.)

(carboxymethyl)ammonium chloride	glycine hydrochloride

(addition of a proton alters the principal group of an amino acid)

1,4-dichlorobenzene (etc.)	*p*-dichlorobenzene (etc.)
2-chlorobuta-1,3-diene	chloroprene

Recommended name	Traditional name(s)
1,2,3,4,5,6-hexa chlorocyclohexane	benzene hexachloride
tri chloroethanal	chloral
2,2,2-tri chloroethanediol	chloral hydrate
1,1,2,2-tetra chloroethane	acetylene tetrachloride
chloroethanoic acid	chloroacetic acid
(di- and tri-chloroethanoic acids similarly.)	
2- chloroethanol	ethylene chlorohydrin
chloroethene	vinyl chloride
1,2- dichloroethene	acetylene dichloride
tri chloromethane	chloroform
tetra chloromethane	carbon tetrachloride
(in an organic context the recommended name is more useful; in a study of Group 14 (Group IV) the traditional name. Probably the number of times the compound is referred to as an organic compound is greater than that as a member of Group 14.)	
(chloromethyl)benzene	benzyl chloride
1- chloro-2-methylbenzene (etc.)	*o*-chlorotoluene (etc.)
(tri chloromethyl)benzene	benzotrichloride
tri chloronitromethane	chloropicrin
3- chloroprop-1-ene	allyl chloride
di copper(I) ethynediiide	cuprous acetylide
decanedioic acid	sebacic acid
decanedioyl dichloride	sebacoyl chloride
(dichloromethyl)benzene	benzal chloride
dodecan-l-ol	lauryl alcohol
epoxyethane	ethylene oxide
epoxypropane	propylene oxide
ethanal	acetaldehyde
ethanal oxime	acetaldoxime; acetaldehyde oxime
ethanal tetramer	metaldehyde
ethanal trimer	paraldehyde
ethanamide	acetamide
ethanedial	glyoxal
ethanediamide	oxamide
ethane-1,2-diamine	ethylenediamine
(this compound, as a ligand, is often denoted by 'en')	
ethanedioic acid	oxalic acid
ethane-1,2-diol	ethylene glycol
ethanethiol	ethyl mercaptan
ethanoates	acetates
ethanoic acid	acetic acid
ethanoic anhydride	acetic anhydride
ethanoic methanoic anhydride	acetic formic anhydride
ethanol	ethyl alcohol; alcohol (ethyl)
ethanenitrile	acetonitrile; methyl cyanide; cyanoethane
ethanoyl chloride	acetyl chloride
2- ethanoyloxybenzenecarboxylic acid	acetylsalicylic acid ('aspirin')
ethene	ethylene
ethenone	ketene
ethenyl-	vinyl-
ethenyl ethanoate	vinyl acetate
(polymers based on this monomer, pva)	
ether (generic name)	ether
ethoxybenzene	phenetole
ethoxyethane	ether; diethyl ether
1,1-di ethoxyethane	acetal

Recommended name	Traditional name(s)
tetra ethoxymethane	ethyl orthocarbonate
tri ethoxymethane	ethyl orthoformate
ethyl benzenecarboxylate	ethyl benzoate
ethyl ethanoate	ethyl acetate
ethyl 3-oxobutanoate	ethyl acetoacetate; acetoacetic ester
(this is the name of the 'keto' form of the ester. If the 'enol' form is specifically meant, its name is ethyl 3-hydroxybut-2-enoate)	
ethylamine	ethylamine
di ethylamine	diethylamine
tri ethylamine	triethylamine
ethylammonium chloride	ethylamine hydrochloride
ethylbenzene	ethylbenzene
tetra ethyllead(IV)	lead tetraethyl
ethyl-lithium	lithium ethyl
(the optional hyphen is inserted for clarity)	
ethylmagnesium bromide	ethyl magnesium bromide
ethyne	acetylene
(acetylene retained in context of welding and oxyacetylene flames)	
fluorescein	fluorescein
fructose	fructose
fulminic acid	fulminic acid
(+)-(D)- glucose	glucose; dextrose
glycogen	glycogen
hexadecanoic acid	palmitic acid
hexadecan-1-ol	cetyl alcohol
cyclo hexadiene-1,4-dione	quinone; p-benzoquinone
hexane	n-hexane
cyclo hexane	cyclohexane; hexahydrobenzene
hexane-1,6-diamine	hexamethylenediamine
hexanedioic acid	adipic acid
hexanedioyl dichloride	adipyl chloride
hexanoic acid	caproic acid
cyclo hexanol	cyclohexanol; hexahydrophenol
cyclo hexene	cyclohexene
hydroxy- (as prefix)	hydroxy-
2- hydroxybenzenecarbaldehyde	salicylaldehyde
2- hydroxybenzenecarboxylic acid	salicylic acid
3,4,5-tri hydroxybenzenecarboxylic acid	gallic acid
3- hydroxybutanal	aldol
(−)-2,3-di hydroxybutanedioic acid	l-tartaric acid; (−)-tartaric acid
meso-2,3-di hydroxybutanedioic acid	mesotartaric acid
(±)-2,3-di hydroxybutanedioic acid	racemic acid; racemic tartaric acid; *dl*-tartaric acid; (±)-tartaric acid
2- hydroxybutanedioic acid	malic acid
3- hydroxybut-2-enoic acid	acetoacetic acid (enol form)
hydroxyethanoic acid	glycollic acid; hydroxyacetic acid
tris(2- hydroxyethyl)amine	triethanolamine
(this name, strictly, is in error because the −OH groups are not given precedence, but it is unambiguous and easier to interpret. The name nitrilotriethanol, while not in error, is likely to be confused by this age group with nitrile, −C≡N, although both include trivalent nitrogen, see Section 6.2.4.)	
4- hydroxy-4-methylpentan-2-one	diacetone alcohol
2- hydroxy-2-methylpropanenitrile	acetone cyanohydrin
2- hydroxy-1,2-diphenylethanone	benzoin
2- hydroxyphenylmethanol	salicyl alcohol

Recommended name	Traditional name
2-hydroxypropane-1,2,3-tricarboxylic acid	citric acid
(the above name is preferred by IUPAC rather than '3-hydroxy-3-carboxypentanedioic acid' in order to treat all the –COOH groups alike)	
2-hydroxypropanoic acid	lactic acid
2-hydroxypropanenitrile	acetaldehyde cyanohydrin
iodomethane	methyl iodide
tri iodomethane	iodoform
2,4-di isocyanato-1-methylbenzene	2,4-tolylene diisocyanate (tdi)
isocyanobenzene	phenyl isocyanide
isocyanoethane	ethyl isocyanide
ketones (generic name)	ketones
lactose	lactose
maltose	maltose
methanal	formaldehyde
methanamide	formamide
methanoic acid	formic acid
methanol	methyl alcohol
methoxybenzene	anisole
methoxyethane	ethyl methyl ether
methoxymethane	dimethyl ether
2-methoxy-2-methylpropane	methyl *tert*-butyl ether
methyl compounds	if not listed, see the corresponding ethyl compound, or, in the case of esters, the parent acid
2-methylpropan-2-yl	*tert*-butyl or *t*-butyl
methyl orange	methyl orange
(most dyes and indicators are compounds whose structures are of no importance in school chemistry. A systematic name can be constructed for each substance if necessary.)	
methylamine	methylamine
methylammonium chloride	methylamine hydrochloride
methylbenzene	toluene
1,2-di methylbenzene (etc.)	*o*-xylene (etc.)
1,3,5-tri methylbenzene	mesitylene
2-methylbenzenecarboxylic acid	*o*-toluic acid
di methyl benzene-1,2-dicarboxylate	dimethyl phthalate
2-methylbenzenesulfonic acid	toluene-*o*-sulphonic acid
3,3-di methylbiphenyl-4,4′-diamine	*o*-tolidine
2-methylbuta-1,3-diene	isoprene
2,2-di methylbutane	neohexane
2,3-di methylbutane-2,3-diol	pinacol
3,3-di methylbutanone	pinacolone
(the numbers may, in fact, be omitted)	
Z-methylbutenedioic acid	citraconic acid
(for the *Z, E* notation see Section 6.5.11)	
3-methylbutyl-	isoamyl-
di methyl ethanedioate	dimethyl oxalate
2-methyl propan-2-yl-	*tert*-butyl- or *t*-butyl-
1-methyl-2-nitrobenzene (etc.)	*o*-nitrotoluene (etc.)
2-methyl-1,3,5-trinitrobenzene	trinitrotoluene
	(tnt in the context of explosives)
2,2,4-tri methylpentane	isooctane
4-methylpent-3-en-2-one	mesityl oxide
2-methylphenol (etc.)	*o*-cresol (etc.)
2-methylphenylamine (etc.)	*o*-toluidine (etc.)
N,N-di methylphenylamine	*N,N*-dimethylaniline

Recommended name	Traditional name
N-methylphenylamine	*N*-methylaniline
2-methylpropane	isobutane
2-methylpropanoic acid	isobutyric acid
2-methylpropan-1-ol	isobutyl alcohol
2-methylpropan-2-ol	*tert*-butyl alcohol
2,2-di methylpropan-1-ol	neopentyl alcohol
2-methylpropene	isobutylene
2-methylpropenoic acid	methacrylic acid
(in the above seven cases, the locant 2 is not strictly necessary and may be omitted)	
2-methylpropyl	isobutyl-
naphthalene	naphthalene
naphthalen-1-amine	a-naphthylamine; l-aminonaphthalene
naphthalene-l-carboxylic acid	α-naphthoic acid
naphthalen-l-ol	α-naphthol
naphthalen-2-ol	β-naphthol
nitrobenzene	nitrobenzene
1,3-di nitrobenzene	*m*-dinitrobenzene
nitromethane	nitromethane
2-nitrophenol (etc.)	*o*-nitrophenol (etc.)
2,4,6-tri nitrophenol	trinitrophenol; picric acid
4-nitrophenylamine	*p*-nitroaniline
1-nitro-2-phenylethene	ω-nitrostyrene
nitroso-	nitroso-
octadecanoic acid	stearic acid
cis-octadec-9-enoic acid	oleic acid
(for introductory work the *cis*- or the -9- or both may be omitted)	
3-oxobutanoic acid	acetoacetic acid (or, specifically, the keto form)
oxoethanoic acid	glyoxalic acid
2-oxopropanoic acid	pyruvic acid
pentane-2,4-dione	acetylacetone
pentanoic acid	*n*-valeric acid
pentyl-	*n*-amyl-
benzeneperoxocarboxylic acid	perbenzoic acid
peroxoethanoic acid	peracetic acid
phenol	phenol
phenolphthalein	phenolphthalein
phenyl- (as a substituent group)	phenyl-
phenylamine	aniline
	(the traditional name is still widely used)
phenylammonium chloride	aniline hydrochloride
N-phenylethanamide	acetanilide; *N*-phenylacetamide
1,2-diphenylethanedione	benzil
phenylethanone	acetophenone
phenylethene	styrene
1,2-di phenylethene	stilbene
phenylhydrazine	phenylhydrazine
N,N′-di phenylhydrazine	hydrazobenzene
phenylmethanol	benzyl alcohol
di phenylmethanone	benzophenone; diphenyl ketone
(phenylmethyl)amine	benzylamine
3-phenylpropenoic acid	cinnamic acid
(related compounds similarly)	

Recommended name	Traditional name

Polymers

All the polymers below are likely to keep their current names when referred to as materials in general use, so that the systematic name is of value mainly to show the monomer/polymer relationship. See Section 6.2.9.

poly(2-chlorobuta-1,3-diene)	neoprene
poly(chloroethene)	polyvinyl chloride; pvc
poly(ethene)	polyethylene (polythene)
poly(ethenol)	polyvinyl alcohol
poly(methanal)	paraformaldehyde
poly(methyl 2-methylpropenoate)	poly(methylmethacrylate); Perspex
poly(phenylethene)	polystyrene
poly(propene)	polypropylene
poly(tetrafluoroethene)	poly(tetrafluoroethylene); ptfe

potassium sodium 2,3-dihydroxybutanedioate	Rochelle salt
propadiene	allene
propanal	propionaldehyde
propanedioic acid	malonic acid
propanenitrile	propionitrile; ethyl cyanide; cyanoethane
propane-1,2,3-triol	glycerol; glycerine
propane-1,2,3-triyl trinitrate	nitroglycerine; glyceryl trinitrate (nitroglycerine, in context of explosives)
propane-1,2,3-triyl trisoctadecanoate (other fats etc. similarly)	glyceryl tristearate; tristearin
propan-1-ol	*n*-propyl alcohol
propan-2-ol	isopropyl alcohol
propanone	acetone (the traditional name is widely used)
propanone oxime	acetoxime, acetone oxime
propan-2-yl	isopropyl-
(propan-2-yl)benzene	cumene, isopropylbenzene
propenal	acrolein
propenoic acid	acrylic acid
prop-2-en-1-ol	allyl alcohol
propenenitrile	acrylonitrile
pyridine	pyridine

rubeanic acid	rubeanic acid

semicarbazide	semicarbazide
semicarbazidium chloride	semicarbazide hydrochloride
disilver(I) ethynediide	silver acetylide
sodium ethoxide	sodium ethoxide; sodium ethylate
sodium phenoxide	sodium phenoxide; sodium phenate
sucrose	sucrose; cane sugar

thiocarbamide *or* thiourea	thiourea
thiols (generic name)	mercaptans; thiols

95

6.4   Traditional names for organic species

6.4.1   Notes

1 Only the C_2 compounds are fully indexed.

2 *see* refers the reader to a note in Section 6.2.2.

3 n.c. means that no change is recommended.

6.4.2   Traditional names: organic

Traditional name	Recommended name
acetal	1,1-diethoxyethane
acetaldehyde	ethanal
acetaldehyde cyanohydrin	2-hydroxypropanenitrile
acetaldehyde oxime	ethanal oxime
acetaldoxime } acetamide	ethanamide
acetanilide	*N*-phenylethanamide
acetates	ethanoates
acetbromamide	*N*-bromoethanamide
acetic acid	ethanoic acid
acetic anhydride	ethanoic anhydride
acetic formic anhydride	ethanoic methanoic anhydride
acetoacetic acid	3-oxobutanoic acid
(unless the enol form, 3-hydroxybut-2-enoic acid, is specifically meant)	
acetoacetic ester *see*	ethyl 3-oxobutanoate
acetone	propanone
acetone cyanohydrin	2-hydroxy-2-methylpropanenitrile
acetone oxime	propanone oxime
acetonitrile	ethanenitrile
acetophenone	phenylethanone
acetoxime	propanone oxime
acetylacetone	pentane-2,4-dione
acetyl chloride	ethanoyl chloride
acetylene	ethyne (or, as generic name, alkyne)
acetylene dichloride	1,2-dichloroethene
acetylene tetrachloride	1,1,2,2-tetrachloroethane
acetylide	ethynediide
acetylsalicylic acid	2-ethanoyloxybenzenecarboxylic acid
(the name 'aspirin' is, of course, appropriate, if the structure is not under discussion)	
acrolein	propenal
acrylic acid	propenoic acid
acrylonitrile	propenenitrile
acyl	n.c.
adenine	n.c.
adenosine	n.c.
adipic acid	hexanedioic acid
adipyl chloride	hexanedioyl dichloride
alanine	2-aminopropanoic acid
alcohol (ethyl)	ethanol
alcohol (wood)	methanol
aldehyde	as generic name, n.c.
aldol	3-hydroxybutanal
aliphatic	n.c.
alkyl	n.c.
allene	propadiene (*or*, as generic name, n.c.)
allyl alcohol	prop-2-en-1-ol
allyl chloride	3-chloroprop-1-ene

Traditional name	Recommended name
amino acids	as a generic name, n.c.
(traditional abbreviations for particular acids are useful in biochemistry)	
p- aminobenzoic acid	4-aminobenzenecarboxylic acid
1- aminonaphthalene	naphthalen-1-amine
o- aminophenol	2-aminophenol
n- amyl-	pentyl-
iso amyl-	3-methylbutyl-
('iso-amyl' often refers to a mixture of isomers, of which 3-methylbutyl is only one)	
aniline	*see* phenylamine
aniline hydrochloride	phenylammonium chloride
anisole	methoxybenzene
anthracene	n.c.
anthranilic acid	2-aminobenzenecarboxylic acid
9,10- anthraquinone	anthracene-9,10-dione
aromatic	n.c.
aryl	n.c.
aspartic acid	aminobutanedioic acid (no numerals needed)

Traditional name	Recommended name
benzal chloride	(dichloromethyl)benzene
benzaldehyde	benzenecarbaldehyde
benzaldoxime	benzenecarbaldehyde oxime
benzamide	benzenecarboxamide
benzene	n.c.
benzenediazonium ion	n.c.
benzene hexachloride	1,2,3,4,5,6- hexachlorocyclohexane
(this name does not distinguish between the geometric isomers)	
benzenesulphonic acid	benzenesulfonic acid
benzidine	biphenyl-4,4'-diamine
benzil	1,2-diphenylethanedione
benzoic acid	benzenecarboxylic acid
benzoin	2-hydroxy-1,2-diphenylethanone
benzonitrile	benzenecarbonitrile
benzophenone	diphenylmethanone
p- benzoquinone	cyclohexadiene-1,4-dione
benzoyl peroxide	di(benzenecarbonyl) peroxide
benzotrichloride	(trichloromethyl)benzene
benzoyl chloride	benzenecarbonyl chloride
benzyl alcohol	phenylmethanol
benzylamine	(phenylmethyl)amine
benzyl chloride	(chloromethyl)benzene
biacetyl	butanedione
biuret	n.c.
bromobenzene	n.c.
bromoform	tribromomethane
N- bromosuccinimide	N-bromobutanedioic imide
butadiene	buta-1,3-diene
n- butane	butane
n- butyl-	butyl-
iso butyl-	2-methylpropyl-
sec- butyl-	butan-2-yl-
tert- butyl-	2-methylpropan-2-yl-
n- butyl alcohol	butan-1-ol
iso butyl alcohol	2-methylpropan-1-ol
sec- butyl alcohol	butan-2-ol
tert- butyl alcohol	2-methylpropan-2-ol
butylene	but-2-ene or but-1-ene, as appropriate
iso butylene	2-methylpropene
n- butyraldehyde	butanal

Traditional name		Recommended name
butyric acid		butanoic acid
calcium carbide		calcium ethynediide (*see* Section 5.2.1)
camphor		n.c.
cane sugar		sucrose
caproic acid		hexanoic acid.
carbamate ion		n.c.
carbamic acid		n.c.
carbamide		n.c.
carbon tetrachloride	*see*	tetrachloromethane
carbonyl chloride		carbonyl dichloride
carboxylic acids		n.c.
catechol		benzene-1,2-diol
cetyl alcohol		hexadecan-1-ol
chloral		trichloroethanal
chloral hydrate		2,2,2-trichloroethanediol
chloroacetic acid		chloroethanoic acid
chloroform		trichloromethane
chloropicrin		trichloronitromethane
chloroprene		2-chlorobuta-1,3-diene
o-chlorotoluene (etc.)		1-chloro-2-methylbenzene (etc.)
cinnamic acid		3-phenylpropenoic acid
(related compounds similarly)		
citraconic acid		2-methylbutenedioic acid
citric acid		2-hydroxypropane-1,2,3-tricarboxylic acid
o-cresol		2-methylphenol
crotonic acid		*trans*-but-2-enoic acid
cumene		prop-2-anylbenzene
cuprous acetylide		dicopper(I) ethynediide
dextrose		(+)-(D)-glucose
diacetone alcohol		4-hydroxy-4-methylpentan-2-one
diacetyl		butanedione
(or *properly* biacetyl)		
p-dichlorobenzene		1,4-dichlorobenzene
(other disubstituted benzene compounds similarly)		
diethyl ether		ethoxyethane
diethylamine		n.c.
dimethylglyoxime		butanedione dioxime
dimethyl oxalate		dimethyl ethanedioate
dimethyl phthalate		dimethyl benzene-1,2-dicarboxylate
N,N-dimethylaniline		*N,N*-dimethylphenylamine
edta	*see*	1,2-bis[bis(carboxymethyl)amino]ethane
eosin		n.c.
ethyl acetate		ethyl ethanoate
(other esters similarly)		
ethyl alcohol		ethanol
ethyl benzene		ethylbenzene
ethyl benzoate		ethyl benzenecarboxylate
ethyl bromide		bromoethane
(other halides similarly)		
ethyl cyanide		propanenitrile
di ethyl ether		ethoxyethane
ethyl isocyanide		isocyanoethane
ethyl magnesium bromide		ethylmagnesium bromide
ethyl methyl ether		methoxyethane
ethyl methyl ketone		butanone
ethyl mercaptan		ethanethiol

Traditional name		Recommended name
ethyl orthocarbonate		tetraethoxymethane
ethyl orthoformate		triethoxymethane
ethylamine		n.c.
ethylene		ethene
ethylene chlorohydrin		2-chloroethanol
ethylenediamine		ethane-1,2-diamine
ethylenediaminetetraacetic acid	*see*	1,2-bis[bis(carboxymethyl)amino]ethane
ethylene dibromide		1,2-dibromoethane
ethylene glycol		ethane-1,2-diol
ethylene oxide		epoxyethane
ethylene ozonide		ethene ozonide
ethylidene dibromide		1,1-dibromoethane
fatty acids		alkanoic acids
fluorescein		n.c.
formaldehyde		methanal
formamide		methanamide
formic acid		methanoic acid
fructose		n.c.
fulminic acid		n.c.
fumaric acid		*trans*-butenedioic acid
gallic acid		3,4,5-trihydroxybenzenecarboxylic acid
glucose		n.c.
glutamic acid		2-aminopentanedioic acid
glycerine }		propane-1,2,3-triol
glycerol		
glyceryl trinitrate		propane-1,2,3-triyl trinitrate
glyceryl tristearate		propane-1,2,3-triyl trioctadecanoate
glycine		aminoethanoic acid
glycine hydrochloride	*see*	(carboxymethyl)ammonium chloride
glycols		(generic name) diols
(and see ethylene glycol above)		
glycollic acid		hydroxyethanoic acid
glyoxal		ethanedial
glyoxalic acid		oxoethanoic acid
hexahydrobenzene		cyclohexane
hexahydrophenol		cyclohexanol
hexamethylenediamine		hexane-1,6-diamine
hexamethylene tetramine		n.c.
hydrazobenzene		*N,N'*-diphenylhydrazine
hydroquinone		benzene-1,4-diol
hydroxy		(no change *in the prefix*)
iodoform		triiodomethane
isoamyl-		3-methylbutyl-
(but is probably a mixture of 'branched pentyl-'s)		
isobutane		2-methylpropane
(the locant is not strictly necessary in this and several following examples)		
isobutyl-		2-methylpropyl-
isobutyl alcohol		2-methylpropan-1-ol
isobutylene		2-methylpropene
isobutyric acid		methylpropanoic acid
isocyanides } as generic name		isocyano-compounds
isonitriles		
iso-octane		2,2,4-trimethylpentane
isophthalic acid		benzene-1,3-dicarboxylic acid

Traditional name		Recommended name
isoprene		methylbuta-1,3-diene
isopropyl-		propan-2-yl-
isopropyl alcohol		propan-2-ol
isopropylbenzene		propan-2-ylbenzene
(related compounds similarly)		
ketene		ethenone
ketones		(as generic name) n.c.
lactic acid		2-hydroxypropanoic acid
lactose		n.c.
lauryl alcohol		dodecan-1-ol
lauroyl peroxide		di(dodecanoyl) peroxide
lead tetraethyl	*see*	tetraethyllead(IV)
lithium ethyl	*see*	ethyl-lithium
litmus		n.c.
maleic acid		*cis*-butenedioic acid
malic acid		2-hydroxybutanedioic acid
malonic acid		propanedioic acid
maltose		n.c.
mercaptans		thiols
mesityl oxide		4-methylpent-3-en-2-one
mesitylene		1,3,5-trimethylbenzene
mesotartaric acid		*meso*-2,3-dihydroxybutanedioic acid
metaldehyde		ethanal tetramer
methacrylic acid		2-methylpropenoic acid
methyl compounds		if not listed, refer above to corresponding ethyl compounds or, in case of esters, to the parent acid
methyl alcohol		methanol
methylamine		n.c.
methylamine hydrochloride		methylammonium chloride
N-methylaniline		*N*-methylphenylamine
methyl *tert*-butyl ether		2-methoxy-2-methylpropane
methyl cyanide		ethanenitrile
di methyl ether		methoxymethane
methyl ethyl ketone (M.E.K.)		butanone
methyl iodide		iodomethane
poly (methyl methacrylate)		poly(methyl 2-methylpropenoate)
methyl orange	*see*	methyl orange
methyl salicylate		methyl 2-hydroxybenzenecarboxylate
naphthalene		n.c.
α-naphthoic acid		naphthalene-1-carboxylic acid
α-naphthol		naphthalen-1-ol
β-naphthol		naphthalen-2-ol
α-naphthylamine		naphthalen-1-amine
neohexane		2,2-dimethylbutane
neopentyl alcohol		2,2-dimethylpropan-1-ol
		(The '2's are not, strictly, necessary)
neoprene		poly(2-chlorobuta-1,3-diene)
ninhydrin		n.c.
p-nitroaniline		4-nitrophenylamine
nitrobenzene		n.c.
nitroglycerine	*see*	propane-1,2,3-triyl trinitrate
nitromethane		n.c.
o-nitrophenol (etc.)		2-nitrophenol (etc.)
nitroso		no change in name of group, as such, but refer to parent compound if necessary

Traditional name	Recommended name
ω- nitrostyrene	1-nitro-2-phenylethene
o- nitrotoluene {etc.}	1-methyl-2-nitrobenzene (etc.)
Nylon	Nylon (trade name)
olefins	alkenes
oleic acid	see cis-octadec-9-enoic acid
any orthocarbonic ester	tetraalkoxymethane
(e.g. ethyl orthocarbonate)	
any orthoformic ester	trialkoxymethane
oxalic acid	ethanedioic acid
oxamide	ethanediamide
palmitic acid	hexadecanoic acid
paraformaldehyde	poly(methanal)
paraldehyde	ethanal trimer
peracetic acid	peroxoethanoic acid
perbenzoic acid	benzeneperoxocarboxylic acid
Perspex	see poly(methyl 2-methylpropenoate)
phenetole	ethoxybenzene
phenol	n.c.
phenolphthalein	n.c.
phenyl	(as substituent group) n.c.
phenylhydrazine	n.c.
phenyl isocyanide	isocyanobenzene
p- phenylenediamine	benzene-1,4-diamine
p- phenylenediamine dihydrochloride	benzene-1,4-diammonium chloride
p- phenylenediamine monohydrochloride	4-aminophenylammonium chloride
phloroglucinol	benzene-1,3,5-triol
phosgene	carbonyl dichloride
phthalic acid	benzene-1,2-dicarboxylic acid
phthalic anhydride	benzene-1,2-dicarboxylic anhydride
phthalimide	benzene-1,2-dicarboximide
picric acid	2,4,6-trinitrophenol
pinacol	2,3-dimethylbutane-2,3-diol
pinacolone	3,3-dimethylbutanone
(numerals may be omitted)	
polypropylene	poly(propene)
ptfe	see poly(tetrafluoroethene)
polythene	see poly(ethene)
polyvinyl alcohol, pva	see poly(ethenol)
polyvinyl chloride, pvc	see poly(chloroethene)
propylene oxide	epoxypropane
pyridine	n.c.
pyrogallol	benzene-1,2,3-triol
pyruvic acid	2-oxopropanoic acid
quinol	benzene-1,4-diol
quinone	cyclohexadiene-1,4-dione
racemic acid	(±)-2,3-dihydroxybutanedioic acid
resorcinol	benzene-1,3-diol
Rochelle salt	potassium sodium 2,3-dihydroxybutanedioate
rubeanic acid	n.c.
salicyl alcohol	2-hydroxyphenylmethanol
salicylaldehyde	2-hydroxybenzenecarbaldehyde
salicylic acid	2-hydroxybenzenecarboxylic acid
sebacic acid	decanedioic acid

Traditional name	Recommended name
sebacoyl chloride	decanedioyl dichloride
semicarbazide	n.c.
semicarbazide hydrochloride	semicarbazidium chloride
semicarbazone	n.c.
silver acetylide	disilver(I) ethynediide (the (I) can usually be omitted)
sodium ethoxide	n.c.
stearic acid	octadecanoic acid
stilbene	1,2-diphenylethene
styrene	phenylethene
succinaldehyde	butanedial
succinic acid	butanedioic acid
succinic anhydride	butanedioic anhydride
sucrose	n.c.
sulphanilamide	4-aminobenzenesulfonamide
sulphanilic acid	4-aminobenzenesulfonic acid
l- tartaric acid	(−)-2,3-dihydroxybutanedioic acid
terephthalic acid	benzene-1,4-dicarboxylic acid
thiourea	thiocarbamide *or* n.c.
o- tolidine	3,3′-dimethylbiphenyl-4,4′-diamine
toluene	methylbenzene
o- toluenesulphonic acid } toluene-*o*-sulphonic acid	2-methylbenzenesulfonic acid
o- toluic acid	2-methylbenzenecarboxylic acid
o- toluidine	2-methylphenylamine
2,4- tolylene diisocyanate	2,4-diisocyanato-1-methylbenzene
triethanolamine	tris-(2-hydroxyethyl)amine
triethylamine	n.c.
TNT	2-methyl-1,3,5-trinitrobenzene *or* tnt
urea	carbamide *or* n.c.
n- valeric acid	pentanoic acid
vinyl acetate	ethenyl ethanoate
vinyl chloride	chloroethene
o- xylene	1,2-dimethylbenzene

6.5 Formulæ and equations

6.5.1 Use of chemical symbols and formulæ

A chemical symbol is used to represent a chemical element or one atom of the element, e.g. H for hydrogen, C for carbon, Cu for copper, and Cl and Br for chlorine and bromine respectively. Symbols for chemical elements are always written in a roman (upright) font.

The practice of using a chemical symbol to represent one mole of an element is incorrect. The same considerations apply to chemical formulæ. The Working Party suggests that chemical symbols and suitable formulæ may be used as a form of shorthand for the names of substances whenever convenient. In many cases a formula is both shorter and more informative than any name in written communication. It is essential, however, that the formula be correct and unambiguous.

6.5.2 State symbols

These provide a convenient notation for indicating the physical states of substances. It is not necessary to delay the introduction of state symbols until chemical formulæ are met; representations such as copper sulfate(s) or copper sulfate(aq) can be used to make clear the difference between these two materials at a very early stage.

The following symbols are recommended:

(s)   solid state
(l)   liquid state
(g)   gaseous state
(aq)   dissolved in water (in quantitative work the symbol implies 'at infinite dilution')

6.5.3 Chemical formulæ of solids

A formula such as $C_6H_{12}O_6$(s) shows the elements present and the atomic proportions in the compound concerned and the physical state, without giving any information about bonding. A formula such as NaCl(s) does *not* imply covalent bonding; it is a perfectly adequate representation for the 'substance in the bottle', and avoids arguments over the extent of ionic character.

If, however, a teacher feels that there are educational advantages in using ionic formulæ for solids, the Working Party recommends that parentheses be used as follows:
sodium carbonate(s) can be represented by

$$(2Na^+ + CO_3^{2-})(s)$$

whilst $2Na_2CO_3$(s) can be represented by

$$2(2Na^+ + CO_3^{2-})(s).$$

If the parentheses are not used then the 2 in front of the unipositive sodium ion can cause confusion and students are inclined to assume that 2 entities of substance are being referred to. The parentheses can also be taken to imply that the ionic species they enclose are 'trapped' together in a crystal structure and are not free to move apart.

Alternative forms such as $2Na^+CO_3^{2-}$ or $Na_2^+CO_3^{2-}$ should not be used. Super- and subscripts should not be 'stacked' in the same vertical line. $Na_2^+CO_3^{2-}$ is preferred, and better still $(Na^+)_2CO_3^{2-}$(s).

Especially when writing answers to examination questions, students become careless in distinguishing between $Na_2^+CO_3^{2-}$ and $Na_2^+CO_3^{2-}$. Students may postulate the existence of ions such as $2Na_2^+$ and can be confused by $Ca^{2+}C_2^{2-}$, $K^+O_2^-$, $Ca^{2+}Cl_2$. If this type of formula is used extensively (and carelessly), examiners could be in the position of having to mark right or wrong variations such as $Ca^{2+}Cl_2^-$, $Ca^{2+}Cl_2$, $Ca^{2+}Cl_2^-$.

Basic student misunderstandings remain undetected if formulæ of this type are used. As a result of these difficulties, some teachers have opted for the form in which, for example, sodium carbonate is written as $(Na^+)_2(CO_3^{2-})$ and this has much to commend it, but the teacher does not have the advantage of implying that the ions are 'trapped' together in the solid state. There is also a tendency to state that compounds such as $(Na^+)_2(CO_3^{2-})$ dissolve in water to give solutions described by $(Na^+)_2(aq)(CO_3^{2-})(aq)$ or $Na_2^+(aq)CO_3^{2-}(aq)$.

The manner of writing formulae illustrated by $(2Na^+ + CO_3^{2-})$(s) and $(Pb^{2+} + 2NO_3^-)$(s) with or without state symbol has none of these disadvantages. It is not suggested that ionic formulæ should always be used for solids that are predominantly ionic, but suggests that *if* ionic formulæ are used they should be of the recommended type.

It may be preferable to talk of Fe^{3+} as 'Fe-three-positive' rather than as 'Fe-three-plus' because 'plus' is a mathematical operation. Similarly O^{2-} may be verbalised as 'oh, two-negative' (*not*, of course, 'oh-two, negative').

6.5.4 Formulae of electrolytes in solution

If the ionic nature of electrolytes in solution is to be stressed, representations such as $H^+(aq) + Cl^-(aq)$ or perhaps $H_3O^+(aq) + Cl^-(aq)$ are recommended. Otherwise HCl(aq) is adequate. They are meant to imply that ions are the predominant species present and that the ions are 'free' from one another. In the case of aqueous sulfuric acid, representations such as $2H^+(aq) + SO_4^{2-}(aq)$ and $H^+(aq) + HSO_4^-(aq)$ may be found useful. $H_2SO_4(l)$ should be used only when referring to the pure acid. Some may wish to use $H_2SO_4(aq)$ to refer to or label the dilute acid since it is otherwise not clear that the diluting agent is water.

6.5.5 Covalent structures

A covalent structure cannot be implied by failing to write an ionic formula as long as formulae showing the relative ratios of the elements in a compound are used. In order to suggest covalency a short single line may be used to represent the pair of electrons in a single bond. Partial charges can be used to denote polar character. Representations such as the following can be used.

$$H \overset{\times\times}{\underset{\times\times}{\times}}Cl\overset{\times}{\times} \quad or \quad H—Cl \quad or \quad H\overset{\delta+}{—}Cl^{\delta-} \quad for \ HCl(g).$$

The use of two *dots* to represent a covalent bond may be confusing because a colon is sometimes met as a representation of a double bond (as in $H_2C\mathbf{:}CH_2$), or is used in other contexts to show a lone pair of electrons. It is usual to use a single dot to represent the unpaired electron of a radical, as in $CH_3•$.

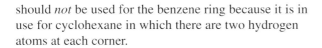

6.5.6 Benzene, cyclohexane and naphthalene

At school level the behaviour of aromatic compounds can be better explained, in the view of the Working Party, if the benzene ring is represented by

rather than by the Kekulé structure, although students should encounter both, and the latter is often useful in representations of reaction mechanisms (as, for instance, in explaining directed substitution). In this representation it is understood that a hydrogen atom is attached to each corner not shown as otherwise occupied.

The representation

should *not* be used for the benzene ring because it is in use for cyclohexane in which there are two hydrogen atoms at each corner.

For naphthalene the Kekulé structure

is preferred, because the circle represents *six* delocalised electrons and in polynuclear hydrocarbons (and derivatives) the number is not six.

6.5.7 Classes of formulae

The following terms for classes of formulae are recognised:

- *Empirical formula* means the *simplest possible* formula showing stoichiometric proportion only. For 2-hydroxypropanoic acid the *empirical* formula is CH_2O.

- *Molecular formula* means, for substances treated as consisting of discrete molecules, the formula in accordance with the correct mass of the molecule. If the molecular complexity varies with temperature the simplest formula may be used for the equilibrium mixture, as with the name (e.g. nitrogen dioxide, NO_2). The *molecular* formula of 2-hydroxypropanoic acid is $C_3H_6O_3$.

■ *Displayed formula* (or *graphic formula*) means a formula in which the spatial arrangement of the atom or groups of atoms and their linkages are projected on to a plane.

Examples:

H — C≡N

hydrogen cyanide   an alkyl ethanoate   2-aminopropanamide

The practice of displaying, for example, the structure of pentane as

rather than as

is to be commended, although it must be recognised that representations such as

2-hydroxypropanoic acid   propanone

do satisfy the criteria for *a full structural formula* in that *all* the bonds between atoms are shown.

It is strongly recommended that hydrogen atoms, if present in the molecule, are *not* omitted from displayed formulae, although the usual school treatment of benzene, etc., is not consistent with this recommendation.

■ *Shortened structural formula* means a formula showing unambiguously, *or by convention*, the sequence and arrangement of the atoms in a molecule in such a way that the nature and position of attachment of each functional group is shown. Examples are

CH$_3$CHOHCOOH   CH$_3$COCH$_3$
or   *or*

CH$_3$CH(OH)CO$_2$H   (CH$_3$)$_2$CO   CH$_3$CH(NH$_2$)CONH$_2$

2-hydroxypropanoic acid   propanone   2-aminopropanamide

The overriding considerations in the use of shortened structural formulae should be clarity and appropriateness in their context. Thus, whilst it is legitimate to shorten the amide group to —CONH$_2$, any multiple carbon–carbon bonds should *always* be shown, as in

CH$_3$[CH$_2$]$_7$CH=CH[CH$_2$]$_7$COOH

octadec-9-enoic acid

■ *Stereochemical formula* means a formula in which any ambiguity which might arise through the existence of stereoisomerism is avoided by use of a suitable convention. There are many different ways of indicating that particular bonds approach, or recede from, the viewer, but **the following are considered appropriate for use** for the 16–19 age range.

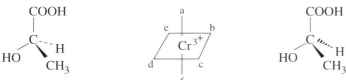

The *tapering zebra* ⁗ is not approved by IUPAC, which prefers equal length lines ▮▮▮▮. Teachers should use their discretion.

The tapering zebra for indicating a bond *receding* from the viewer may be less easily confused with the *solid wedge* ◣ in general use for bonds *in front of* the paper than a 'reversed solid wedge'

could be, as in

It is, however, recommended that models be used wherever possible in conjunction with such representations.

6.5.8   Fischer projections

In addition to the above 'perspective formulae' students may encounter 'projection formulae' but these are not recommended for use at the 16–19 age level. In *Fischer projections* the longest carbon chain is drawn vertically with the carbon atom in the highest oxidation state at the top. The two bonds drawn horizontally are considered to come towards the viewer out of the plane of the paper, and the vertical bonds are considered to recede from the viewer. The Fischer projection:

A

represents the molecule which could be depicted by either of the perspective formulae, **B**.

B

One function of Fischer projections is to establish the relationship between different stereoisomers. The interchange of any pair of groups in the projection represents a change of configuration, and a second interchange about the same 'chiral centre' returns the

depicted molecule to the original configuration. Care must be taken, however, in relating Fischer projections to perspective formulae and reference should be constantly made to models. The perspective formula **C** as depicted:

C

also bears a superficial resemblance to projection **A**. The Fischer projection corresponding to **C** is, however, **D**, as construction of a model will show.

D

Comparison of **D** with **A** shows that the perspective **C** denotes the *enantiomer* of **A**. Thus, if Fischer projections are being used it may be helpful to use perspective formulae of type **B**, rather than the more generally preferred type **C**.

6.5.9   Stereoisomers

Stereoisomers which are mirror-images of each other are termed *enantiomers*. Enantiomers always display equal and opposite optical activity. An optically-active compound *may* possess a stereoisomer which is optically *inactive*. Any stereoisomers which do *not* bear a mirror-image relationship to each other are termed *diastereoisomers*.

The isomers of 2,3-dihydroxybutanedioic acid provide an example; the optically inactive diastereoisomer is the so-called *meso*-isomer which is able to adopt a geometry having a plane of symmetry as shown here.

An optically-active substance producing a clockwise rotation (dextrorotation), as seen by the observer using the polarimeter, is denoted as the (+)-enantiomer, e.g. (+)-glucose. The *lævo* form is denoted by (−)-, e.g. (−)-glucose. At one time these were known respectively as *d*-glucose and *l*-glucose (and still are by biologists).

6.5.10 Absolute configuration

The three-dimensional arrangement in space of the groups attached to a 'chiral' (asymmetric) carbon atom has been conventionally denoted on the basis of any structural relationship to one or other of the enantiomers of 2,3-dihydroxypropanal (glyceraldehyde).

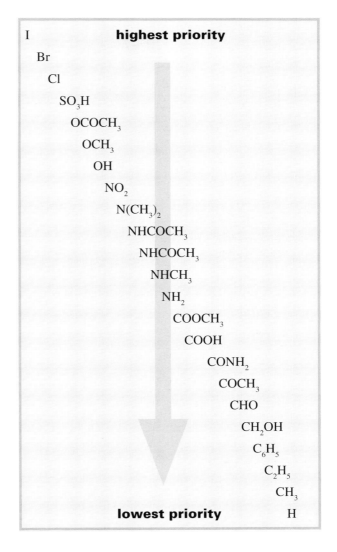

highest priority

I
Br
Cl
SO_3H
$OCOCH_3$
OCH_3
OH
NO_2
$N(CH_3)_2$
$NHCOCH_3$
$NHCOCH_3$
$NHCH_3$
NH_2
$COOCH_3$
COOH
$CONH_2$
$COCH_3$
CHO
CH_2OH
C_6H_5
C_2H_5
CH_3

lowest priority   H

D-2,3-dihydroxypropanal   L-2,3-dihydroxypropanal
D-glyceraldehyde   L-glyceraldehyde
S-2,3-dihydroxypropanal   R-2,3-dihydroxypropanal

Any optically-active compound having a configuration related to D-glyceraldehyde is denoted by the prefix 'D-' and correspondingly with the 'L-' form. The 'D/L' system is of limited application.

The current and more versatile 'R/S' nomenclature is gaining favour in 16–19 chemistry.

According to the R/S convention the groups that might be attached to a chiral centre are listed in an order of priority based on the atomic number of the atom so attached.

The order from highest to lowest priority is shown in the box opposite.

The 'chiral' carbon atom is viewed from such a direction that the substituent of *lowest* priority in the above list is hidden directly behind it and the other three are in front of it. If their descending order of priority (1 - - 2 - - 3) traces a right-handed (clockwise) path, then the centre is given the prefix 'R-' (from the Latin *rectus* = right). If the descending order of priority traces an anticlockwise path the prefix 'S–' (*sinister* = left) is attached.

It is not possible to infer from the observed optical rotatory power of a substance its absolute configuration.

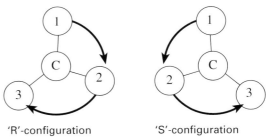

'R'-configuration   'S'-configuration

6.5.11 *Cis–trans* (geometric) isomers

The familiar *cis–trans* nomenclature is adequate for compounds such as

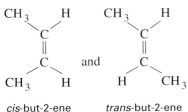

cis-but-2-ene   *trans*-but-2-ene

but is not capable of dealing with

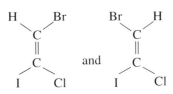

and

A recent and more versatile convention (Z/E for *zusammen/entgegen*) names such compounds by means of an order of priority of groups as used in the *R/S* system (see Section 6.5.10) but this is probably too complex for the 16–19 age group.

In applying the *Z/E* convention to stereoisomerism at a double bond, the designation *Z* or *E* depends on whether the group of higher priority attached to one end of the double bond is on the same (*Z*) or the opposite side (*E*) from the group of higher priority attached to the other end. Thus in the case of above trihalogenoethenes the isomer cited first may be designated *E* (Br and I on opposite sides) and that cited second, *Z*.

It is recommended, however, that in such cases names should be avoided and the distinction be made by means of structural formulae of the type shown above.

Representations such as

$$CH_3 - \underset{\underset{H}{|}}{C} = \overset{\overset{H}{|}}{C} - CH_3$$

should be avoided. The distortion of the bond angle is both unnecessary and confusing.

6.5.12   Chemical equations

The requirement that an equation should balance does not preclude the use of chemical formulae in statements of reaction schemes or summaries which are not balanced. Likewise 'half-equations' for redox reactions need not necessarily be added to give a final equation. For the reaction of magnesium with hydrochloric acid, equations such as the following are suitable:

$$Mg(s) + 2H^+(aq) + 2Cl^-(aq) \rightarrow Mg^{2+}(aq) + 2Cl^-(aq) + H_2(g)$$

or $Mg(s) + 2H^+(aq) \rightarrow Mg^{2+}(aq) + H_2(g)$

or $Mg(s) \rightarrow Mg^{2+}(aq) + 2e^-$

$$2e^- + 2H^+(aq) \rightarrow H_2(g)$$

It is permissible to use an equals sign = in place of an arrow in writing a *balanced* equation. An equals sign should *never* be used in reaction schemes which have not been balanced. It must never be suggested that equations or half-equations necessarily represent the mechanism by which the reaction proceeds.

6.5.13   Stoichiometric calculations from equations

A chemical formula (or atomic symbol for an element) represents a single chemical entity. The formula does not by itself represent 1 mol of that entity. Likewise an equation refers to the entities involved and not to 1 mol of the reaction represented by it. The necessary logical connection between the physical quantity 'amount of substance' (of which the SI base unit is the mole) and the 'stoichiometric coefficient' is provided by the fact that the amount of substance of a specified entity *is proportional to the number* of the specified entities under consideration.

Students should be aware that, essentially, stoichiometric equations are derived experimentally. For example, it could be established by experiment that:

     3.25 g of zinc react with 1.60 g of sulfur to give 4.85 g of zinc sulfide

$\Rightarrow$ 65.0 g of zinc react with 32.0 g of sulfur to give 97.0 g of zinc sulfide

Using the molar mass values $M(Zn) = 65$ g mol^{-1}, and $M(S) = 32$ g mol^{-1} it follows that:

$\Rightarrow$ 1 mol of zinc reacts with 1 mol of sulfur to give 97.0 g of zinc sulfide

On this evidence the *empirical* formula of zinc sulfide is established as ZnS and, of course, the molar mass of the entity ZnS is 97.0 g mol^{-1}. In the absence of any evidence that the substance zinc sulfide might better be represented as, e.g. Zn_2S_2 or Zn_3S_3, the equation:

     $Zn + S \rightarrow ZnS$

is accepted as best representing the stoichiometry of the reaction.

Having once established a stoichiometric formula or equation, similar logic may be applied in reverse so that the reacting quantities, measured by amount (of substance), can be calculated at will.

Example 1

$$Zn(s) \quad + \quad S(s) \quad \rightarrow \quad ZnS(s)$$

$\Rightarrow$ 1 entity Zn reacts with 1 entity S to give 1 entity ZnS

$\Rightarrow$ $1/y$ mol of Zn reacts with $1/y$ mol of S to give $1/y$ mol of ZnS

(choosing y so that $1/y$ mol of any entity contains just 1 entity. It is usual to omit this step.)

$\Rightarrow$ 1 mol of Zn reacts with 1 mol of S to give 1 mol of ZnS

$\Rightarrow$ 65 g of Zn reacts with 32 g of S to give 97 g of ZnS

(The numerical value of y is approximately 6.022×10^{23}: $y/L = 1$ mol.)

Example 2

$MgCO_3 + 2HCl \rightarrow MgCl_2 + H_2O + CO_2$

$\Rightarrow$ 1 mol of $MgCO_3$ reacts with 2 mol of HCl

$\Rightarrow$ 84 g of $MgCO_3$ reacts with 2.00 dm^3 of a solution for which $c(HCl) = 1.00$ mol dm^{-3}

$\Rightarrow$ 2.1 g of $MgCO_3$ reacts with $\dfrac{2.1 \times 2000}{84}$ cm^3 of HCl ($c = 1.00$ mol dm^{-3})

or, similarly, with $\dfrac{2.1 \times 2000 \times 1.00}{84 \times 0.02}$ cm^3 of HCl ($c = 0.02$ mol dm^{-3})

Example 3

$MgCO_3 + 2HCl \rightarrow MgCl_2 + H_2O + CO_2$

1 mol of $MgCO_3$ yields 1 mol of CO_2

84 g of $MgCO_3$ yields (2.24×10^{-2}) m^3 of CO_2 at s.t.p. (1 atm pressure and 273 K)

2.1 g of $MgCO_3$ yields $\dfrac{2.1 \times 2.24 \times 10}{84}$ dm^3 of CO_2 at s.t.p. (1 atm pressure and 273 K)

The calculation of the quantity of CO_2 obtained by a given amount of HCl(aq) may be performed in a similar manner. It is recommended that calculations are not shortened to an extent greater than in examples 2 and 3.

It may be noted from example 3, in which the reaction involves a reactant in solution, that it is often difficult to establish by direct measurement the stoichiometry of *every* entity involved (water in this example). The full stoichiometric equation may be deduced in such cases by resorting to the conservation principle underlying the idea of chemical equations being balanced.

6.5.14 Spectator ions

The term spectator ions is used to describe those ions which are not directly involved in a reaction between solutions of electrolytes.

For example, in the following equation Na$^+$(aq) and Cl$^-$(aq) are spectator ions.

$$H^+(aq) + Cl^-(aq) + Na^+(aq) + OH^-(aq) \rightarrow H_2O(l) + Na^+(aq) + Cl^-(aq)$$

Spectator ions need not be included in the equation unless they are necessary for the purposes of noting the conditions or because they affect the enthalpy, extent or rate of the reaction.

For example, in the case of the reaction denoted by

$$Ba^{2+}(aq) + SO_4^{2-}(aq) \rightarrow (Ba^{2+} + SO_4^{2-})(s)$$

$$\text{or } BaSO_4(s)$$

when 1 mol dm^{-3} solutions of $BaCl_2$ and H_2SO_4 are mixed, approximately twice as much energy is released as when the same volumes of solutions of $BaCl_2$ and Na_2SO_4 of concentration 1.00 mol dm^{-3} are used, and the spectator ions ought therefore to be shown if energy changes are being considered.

6.5.15   Chemical equilibria and reversible reactions

When it is important to stress that a reaction does not go to completion $\rightleftharpoons$ can be used.

$\rightleftharpoons$ or $\rightleftharpoons$ can be used to imply which species predominate at equilibrium. Two full arrows as in

$$\text{Ni} + 4\text{CO} \underset{200\,°C}{\overset{60\,°C}{\rightleftarrows}} \text{Ni(CO)}_4$$

may be used to denote a reaction which may proceed in

either direction according to the conditions but is not necessarily at equilibrium. The conditions should, preferably, be indicated.

6.5.16   Mechanistic equations

When using a mechanistic approach to organic chemistry, the shift of two electrons should be shown by a *curly arrow* $\curvearrowright$ starting where the electron pair is before reaction and pointing to its destination. It is often helpful to draw any lone pair involved. The arrow indicates a complete shift and not merely a polarisation.

For example, the heterolytic fission of the carbon-halogen bond to give a carbocation and a halide ion, can be shown by:

The term carbocation (rather than 'carbonium ion') is preferred for cations in which the positive charge may be regarded as being carried by a carbon atom, as above.

Similarly the term carbanion is used where the negative charge of an anion may be regarded as being carried by a carbon atom, as in $(C_6H_5)_3C^-$.

During homolytic bond fission the movement of a single electron can be depicted by a half-arrow (sometimes called a *fish-hook arrow*).

Delocalisation of electrons may be depicted, if desired, by dotted lines, as in:

Mechanistic equations involving the benzene ring may be depicted by means of notations such as:

or

The partial circle in the Wheland intermediate shown, represents the limits of delocalisation of the four remaining π electrons.

7 LATIN AND GREEK COMPONENTS OF WORDS

7.1 Word roots

Many technical terms are derived from Latin and Greek roots, particularly in Biology. Most can be used either as prefixes or suffixes – thus cytology and phagocyte. The 'root' here is **cyt** meaning cell and various letter additions are made to facilitate pronunciation ('cytlogy' and 'phagocyt', or 'phagcyt', would be very awkward).

In the list below the main word components are given as roots, followed in parentheses by some of the various terminations they may have. Some roots are usually used only as prefixes or as suffixes and these are therefore given only in these forms. The meanings may

not be the literal classical translations but each is the meaning currently accepted in scientific terms.

Be careful of pairs of similar prefixes (ante-, anti-; homo-, homeo-; phyllo-, phylo-; pro-, proto-). American textbooks often replace æ and œ by e (e.g. hem for hæm), though the spellings eco- and fetus for the older œco- and fœtus are well established in English usage.

Some of the word roots listed are from languages other than Latin and Greek.

Numerical prefixes are given in Section 7.2.

Component	Meaning
a- (an- before vowels)	not
ab-	away
ablat-	carry away
-aceous	like
actin-	light
adip-	fat
ad-	towards, to
aem *see* haem	blood
aer (aero-)	air, oxygen
agr (agri-)	field
alb-	white
allel (allelo-)	different
allo-	different, opposing, a variation of
amphi-	both
andr (andro-)	male
angi (angio-, -angium)	container
ante-	before
anth (antho-, -anthus)	flower
anti-	against, opposing, counteracting, neutralising
aqua	indicating, relevant to, water
arch	primitive
arthr (arthro-)	joint
-ase	an enzyme
astr	star
aut (auto-)	self
aux	growth
bar	heavy
bathy-	deep
bi (bio-, -biotic, -be)	life
(*but* bi- also = two)	
-blast	budding

Component	Meaning
calci-	lime
carcin-	cancer
cardi (cardio-, -cardiac)	heart
cata-	down
carn (carni-)	flesh, meat
cera-	horn (material)
chalc-	copper (note: the name 'chalcogens' for the elements in Group 16 (Group VI), O, S, etc., is derived from the Latin calx = 'lime')
chemo-	involving chemicals or chemical reactions
chlor (chloro-)	green
chondr (chondro-)	cartilage
chrom (chromo-, -chrome)	colour
chron	time
-cide	killing
cis-	same side
-clase	cleavage
clast- (-clast)	broken
co-	with
contra-	against
cosmo-	universe
cost (costo-, -costal)	rib
counter-	opposing
-crin	secrete
cryo-	cold
cyan	blue
cyst (cysto-)	bladder
cyt (cyto-, -cyte)	cell
de-	undo
dendr	tree, branch
dent	tooth

Component	Meaning
derm (dermo-)	skin
dextr-	right (handed)
dia-	across
diplo-	double
dors (dorso-, -dorsal)	the back
dys-	bad
ec (eco-)	dwelling
ecto-	outside
-ectomy	cutting out
en-	in
encephal	brain
endo-	inside
enter (entero-)	gut
epi-	above
erg-	work
erythro-	red
eu-	good
ex-	away
extra-	beyond
flag-	whip
flav-	yellow
-fugal	fleeing
gam (gamo-, -gamy)	mating
gaster (gastro-)	stomach
ge (geo-)	the earth
gen (geno-, -gen, -genetic)	forming
gon	reproduction
-gram	written
graph (grapho-, -graphic)	write
gyn	female
gyro-	circle
haem, aem (haemo-, -aemic)	blood
halo-	salt
haplo-	single
hepat-	liver
herb (herbi-)	plant
hetero-	different
holo-	complete
homeo-, homoio-	constant
homo-	the same
hydr (hydro-, -hydric)	water
hygro-	wet
hyper-	excess
hypo-	below
-ia	(often) a disease
ichthy (ichthyo-, -ichthyes)	fish
im-	not
-in	(usually) a protein
infra-	under
inter-	between
intra-	within
insul	island
iso-	the same

Component	Meaning
-ite	rock
-itis	an inflammation
kary (karyo-, -karyotic)	nucleus
kin-, kinet-	motion
labia-, labio-	lip
lact-	milk
laev-	left (handed)
leuc-	white
lig-	bind
lign (ligni-)	wood
lip-	fat
litho- (-lite)	stone
log (-logy)	study
lys (lyso-, -lysis)	breakdown
macro-	large
mega-	large
mel (melan-)	black
meningo-	membrane
meso-	middle
meta-	after
-metry	measure
micro-	small
mit-	thread
-mnaesia	memory
muc-	slime
morph	form, shape
mut-	change
myc (myco-, -mycetes)	fungus
myl-	mill, grind
myo-	muscle
necro-	corpse
neo-	new
neur (neuro-)	nerve
noct-	night
nucleo-	kernel
ob-	against
-oid	resembling
oligo-	few
-oma	tumour
omni-	all
-on	a unit
oo-	egg
opt	sight
ophthalm	eye
orb-	circle
orni-	bird
ortho-	straight
-ose	a carbohydrate
-osis	a phenomenon
osmo-	push
oste (osteo-)	bone
ovi-, ovu-	egg

Component	Meaning
pach- (-pach)	thick
paed (paedo-)	child
palaeo-	ancient
pan-	all
para-	beside
partheno-	without fertilisation
path (patho-, -pathic, -pathy)	disease
ped	foot/leg
peri-	around
-petal	seeking
petro-	rock
phae (phaeo-)	brown
phag (phago-, -phage)	eating
pharmaco-	drug
phen (pheno-)	appearance
phil	liking
phob	fear
phon	sound
phospho-	containing phosphorus or relevant to light
phot (photo-)	light
phyl (phylo-)	race, group
phyll (phyllo-, -phyll)	leaf
phyt (phyto-, -phyte)	plant
piezo-	squeeze
plan	flat
pneum-	air
-pnoea	breathing
pod (podo-)	foot/leg
post-	after
pro-	before
proto-	first
pseud	false
pyr-	fire

Component	Meaning
radio-	ray
ren-	kidney
reticul-	network
rheo-	flow
rhin-	nose
rhizo-	root
rhod (rhodo-)	pink

Component	Meaning
sacchar-	sugar
sarco-	flesh
sapr (sapro-)	decay
schizo-	split
scler-	hard
seb-	oil
seism-	shake
sesqui-	one and a half
sider	iron
-sis	a condition
som (somat-, -some)	a body
sperm	seed
spir (spiro-, -spire)	breathe
spor-	seed
squam-	scale

Component	Meaning
stas	halt
stat (stato-, -static)	stability
stereo-	solid
strato-	spread out
stoma	mouth
stria-	groove
sub-	under
super-, supra-	above
sym-, syn-	together with, same
systol-	contraction

Component	Meaning
tauto-	the same
tax (taxo-)	arrangement
telo-	end
therm (thermo-)	heat
thio-	sulfur
thromb	clot
tom (-tome, -tomy)	cut
ton	strength
tox	poison
trans-	across
tribo-	rubbing
trich-	hair
-tron	device
trop (-tropic)	moving
troph (-trophic)	feeding

Component	Meaning
ultra-	beyond

Component	Meaning
-valent	strength
vas (vaso-)	vessel
ventr	belly
ves	blister, bladder
vita	life
vitro	glass
vivi–	living
vor (-vore, -vorous)	feeding

Component	Meaning
xantho-	yellow
xeno-	strange, foreign
xer (xero-)	dry
xyl (xylo-)	wood

Component	Meaning
zoo	animal
zyg (zygo-)	fused together
zym (zymo-, -zyme)	yeast (but more usually enzyme)

Note on diminutive endings: There is a whole range of suffixes which when added to a stem mean a small version of the object: they all contain the letter 'l'. The commonest is -**icle** as in cuticle (= 'small skin'), radicle (= 'small root'), ventricle (= 'small belly') etc.

The others, such as -olus, -ula, -ellum, vary the Latin ending (-us, -a, -um) according to the gender of the word, or can have the anglicised forms -ole, -ule, -elle (e.g. arteriole, venule, organelle).

7.2   Numerical prefixes

Both Latin and Greek sets of numerical prefixes are used in science but care should be taken that this use is consistent. A look at the 'two-' prefixes will show which set is used with which word. Thus bilateral, bilobed, biped, bisect imply the Latin prefixes and dimer, dioxide imply the Greek ones. Chemical numerical prefixes follow the Greek set.

Sometimes two words of otherwise identical derivation may have slightly different meanings; thus quadruped and tetrapod both mean 'four-limbed' but the former implies that all four limbs are legs. A bird is thus a tetrapod but not a quadruped.

Number	Latin	Greek
half	semi-	hemi-
one	uni-	mono-
one and a half	sesqui-	
two	bi-	di-
three	tri-	tri-
four	quadri-, quadru-	tetra-
five	quinque-	penta-
six	sex-	hexa-
seven	sept-	hepta-
eight	oct-	octa-
nine	nov-	ennea-
ten	dec-	deka-, deca-
many	multi-	poly-

7.3   The Greek alphabet

Letters are used to represent physical quantities in equations, and so on. There are not enough letters to use a different one for each quantity. In the Latin alphabet there are 26 capital and 26 small letters, but since both O and o can too easily be confused with 0 we end up with 50. The Greek alphabet has 24 capital and 24 small letters. Some, especially capitals, are the same as the Latin letters; some, capital and small, are very much alike; some are awkward to write accurately. In the table below, those marked * are not generally used for one of these three reasons. Modern Greek pronunciation differs markedly from 'scientific', especially for β, χ and τ.

Greek capital letter	Greek small letter	Greek name	Modern Greek pronunciation	English nearest sound	as in
A*	α	alpha	**a**lfa	a	man
B*	β	beta	v**i**ta	v	vase
Γ	γ	gamma	g**a**ma	g (soft rolled g)	sugar
Δ	δ	delta	th**e**lta	th	then
E*	ε	epsilon	**e**psilon	e	let
Z*	ζ*	zeta	z**i**ta	z	zebra
H*	η	eta	**i**ta	i (clipped)	feet
ϑ*	ϑ	theta	th**i**ta	th	thick
I*	ι*	iota	y**o**ta	y	yacht
K*	κ	kappa	k**a**pa	k	king
Λ*	λ	lambda	l**a**mtha (th = then)	l	ladder
M*	μ	mu	m**i**	m	mum
N*	ν	nu	ny**i**	n	no
Ξ*	ξ*	xi	ks**i**	ks	box
O*	o*	omicron	**o**mikron	o	not
Π*	π	pi	p**i**	p	par
P*	ρ	rho	r**o**	r	rabbit
Σ	s* *or* σ	sigma (1)	s**i**gma (soft g)	s	sun
T*	τ	tau	t**u**f	t	top
Y*	υ*	upsilon	**i**psilon	i	India
Φ	φ*	phi	f**i**	f	far
X*	χ	chi (hard ≡ K)	h**i**	hee (voiceless) *or* (Scots) loch	hue
Ψ*	ψ	psi	ps**i**	ps	taps
Ω	ω*	omega	om**e**ga (soft g)	o	orange

Note: Vowels pronounced in Greek are short and clipped. For example: i not as ee but shorter, almost i; the name rho not as r<u>oe</u> but stopping short as r<u>o</u> as in r<u>o</u>b. The vowel stressed is printed in bold.

(1) σ used in the middle of words and s used at the ends of words.

8 GLOSSARY

8.1 Introduction

Chapter 8 and its companion Chapter 9 ('Minefield') are complementary.

The Glossary is targeted at those teachers who are teaching just inside – or sometimes just outside – the limits of their specialist knowledge. The Working Party is here thinking of the chemist teaching the Soil Science or Biochemistry options at A-level, the geologist the former, and the physicist or chemist coping with aspects of Materials. Such teachers might welcome some guidance with technical terms.

The Minefield is written for those specialists who have perhaps become over-familiar with their subject and as a result have begun to use words loosely or over-simply or ambiguously or even wrongly. Of course none of those reading this book think that this would apply to them! Nevertheless at least two of the Working Party confess to fallibility on these lines. It is hoped therefore that this section will be thought-provoking and useful for all those who dip into it.

In Chapters 8 and 9 the sequence is that of the topics listed in Chapter 2; items are usually arranged alphabetically within each topic. Where a word is used with a different meaning in another branch of science, it is cross-referred to the appropriate sub-section (e.g. 'see 8.2F'). Similarly a reference to the Minefield is given as, e.g. 'see 9.2F'.

Sub-sections in which there is at the moment no entry are still listed because in later editions they might be used (and to correlate with Chapters 2 and 3).

8.2A Length and time

half-life	The half-life of a population with respect to some change is the average time taken for the population to fall **to** half as a result of that change. The population needs to be large so that chance fluctuations can be ignored. The 'three-quarters-life' or 'one nth-life', similarly, give the time taken for the population to drop **to** three-quarters or **to** one nth, respectively, of the original size. In the context of radioactivity, take care not to refer to 'the radioactivity' dropping – the half-life of ^{238}U, for example, is 4.51×10^9 years but the products of the decay are themselves radioactive so 'the radioactivity of a specimen of ^{238}U' includes the emissions from the products. The half-life of ^{238}U is then the time taken for the radioactivity due to that isotope to fall to half its original value *or* the time taken for the number of atoms of that isotope to fall to half its original value.

8.2B Motion, mass and force

action/reaction	See 9.2B	levers	See 9.2B
amplitude	See 9.2B and 9.2N	momentum	See 9.2B
centrifugal/centripetal forces	See 9.2B	Newton's Third Law	See 9.2B
force diagrams	See 9.2B	tension/compression	See 9.2B
frame of reference	See 9.2B	speed/velocity of light	See 9.2B
friction/grip	See 9.2B	weight	See 9.2B
fulcrum/pivot	See 9.2B	weightlessness	See 9.2B

8.2C Changing direction

8.2D Energy

energy transfer diagrams	See 9.2D
transfer/transform	See 9.2D

8.2E Heat

critical temperature	The temperature above which a gas cannot be liquefied by pressure alone. Above the critical temperature there is no distinction between the liquid and vapour states.
enthalpy, H	This term refers to measurements involving heat content made at a fixed temperature and pressure; see also internal energy below.
'heat' used as a noun	See 9.2E
'heat' used as a verb	See 9.2E
internal energy, U	This term refers to measurements involving heat content made at a fixed temperature and volume.

8.2F Molecular properties

amount of substance	See 9.2F	molar mass	See 9.2F
molar	See 9.2F	molecular entity	See 9.2F

8.2G Chemical reactions

acidic	See 9.2G and 9.2N	plastic	See 9.2G and 9.2N
atomic structure	See 9.2G and 9.2N	plasticiser	See 9.2G
basic	See 9.2G and 9.2N	pure	See 9.2G
Brønsted-Lowry	See 9.2G	solid solution	See 9.2G and 9.2N
concentration	See 9.2G	species	See 9.2G, 9.2M and 9.2N
intermediate	See 9.2G and 9.2N	surfactant	See 9.2G
octane rating	See 9.2G	volatiles	See 9.2G and 9.2N
osmosis	See 9.2G		

8.2H Material properties

cementation	See 9.2H and 9.2N
ductile/malleable	See 9.2H and plastic, 9.2N
hardness	See 9.2H and 9.2N

8.2I Electricity

electricity	See 9.2I
emf/pd	See 9.2I

8.2J Electric and magnetic fields
8.2K Electrochemistry

cell reactions and cell diagrams	See 9.2K.1
electrode potentials	See 9.2K.2
Faraday constant	See 9.2K.3

8.2L Sound

loudness

The loudness of a sound is a measure of a listener's subjective response and is related to the intensity of the sound. The intensity of the sound is measured in W m^{-2}.

The normal ear is most sensitive to frequencies of around 2 kHz. At this frequency the weakest pure note discernible is at a continuous intensity of about 10^{-12} W m^{-2}. This value is taken as the **standard intensity** against which all others are compared.

At any particular intensity, I, the **intensity level** is defined as

$$\log_{10} \frac{I}{I_0} \text{ bel, where } I_0 \text{ is taken as } 1 \times 10^{-12} \text{ W m}^{-2}$$

As the bel is such a huge jump we prefer to measure intensity levels in decibel, dB: i.e.

intensity level = $10 \log_{10} \frac{I}{I_0}$ dB. Note that 1 dB represents an increase in intensity by a factor of 1.26, which is considered the smallest detectable change in intensity. 3 dB represents a doubling in intensity.

The unit of loudness level of a pure note is the **phon**. The 'zero phon curve' (frequency curve) represents the threshold of hearing of a normal human ear. The phon scale is chosen to be numerically equal to the decibel scale of intensity level at 1 kHz. For any other particular frequency the loudness has to be matched to the perceived loudness of a reference tone of 1 kHz.

Note that because loudness depends upon frequency it will depend also on whether the sound is a pure note or a mixture of frequencies.

At very low and very high frequencies the threshold intensity rises considerably. At 200 Hz, for example, and at 10 kHz, the threshold intensity for someone with normal hearing is about 10^{-10} W m^{-2}; i.e. about one hundred times the threshold intensity at 2 kHz.

Permanent loss of hearing results from continuous or habitual exposure to excessively intense noise. (This includes very loud music.) Higher frequencies are especially damaging. The effect is cumulative – and not immediately apparent unless the sound is 'explosive'. The medical profession will recognise here the cause of 'boiler-maker's disease'.

For intensity level data see Section 3.2L.1.

8.2M Biology

NOTE: in this sub-section items are arranged by topic rather than in alphabetical order.

8.2M.1 Ecology

Ecology is the study of the relationships between organisms and their environment (which of course includes other organisms).

The **environment** is everything that influences the life of an organism.

The **habitat** is the place where an organism lives; it has a physical location which is characterised by physical influences (**abiotic**) such as climate and the nature of the soil and/or rocks, and the biological influences (**biotic**) of the other organisms which live there.

A **microhabitat** is just a very small habitat. The idea of a microhabitat is important because it is easy to forget that conditions such as temperature, for example, can vary enormously over small distances, e.g. from the base to the tip of a grass leaf.

A **niche** is defined by the biology of an organism, its lifestyle and the habitat it lives in. For example, bluebells and beech trees are both found in a woodland habitat but the bluebell completes its life cycle above ground early, before the beech tree has come into leaf. The two plants occupy different niches.

A **potential niche** is the theoretical range of habitats, with appropriate physical and biotic constraints, within an ecosystem (see below) where a given organism could survive.

A **realised niche** is the actual, more restricted, combination of habitat, physical and biotic conditions which an organism occupies. Some organisms can occupy the same niche in different habitats e.g. pond snails graze on vegetation in ponds; limpets graze on vegetation on a sea-shore.

A **population** is the total number of individuals of the same species which live within a habitat.

A **community** is all the living organisms, of different species, which live together and interact in a habitat.

An **ecosystem** is the complex association of plants, animals and micro-organisms in a particular habitat which interact with each other and with their abiotic (non-living) habitat. The organisms may compete for resources or feed off one another.

A **biome** is the group of similar environments which exist in different places on the earth. A biome is basically defined by the dominant vegetation type, e.g. tropical rain forest or savannah.

The **biosphere** is the total of the land, seas and atmosphere above which supports life.

Succession describes the changes in a community over time. Starting perhaps with bare ground, colonising plants are the first to invade. These provide food and shelter for other organisms which join the community. New, larger and stronger plants take over as the dominant species, being able to thrive in the shelter and biotic changes brought about by the colonisers. Over time the community stabilises with one or two dominant plant species.

When stable, the community is called a **climax community**. Such a community is more diverse in its range of species than any earlier stage and is more stable; abiotic factors have less overall influence.

trophic level, etc.

Trophic means 'pertaining to food or nutrition'.

Trophic levels are one way of describing feeding relationships in an ecosystem: they describe one step in a food chain. Green plants which capture light energy by photosynthesis are the first trophic level. Since they do not feed on other organisms they are called **producers**. Organisms which feed on plants or other animals are called **consumers**.

Organisms which feed specifically on plants are called **primary consumers** or **first-order consumers**.

Organisms which feed on primary consumers are called **secondary consumers** or **second-order consumers**. This sequence is repeated, generally no further than **fourth-order** consumers because by the fourth order the animal cannot cover enough ground to find sufficient third-order consumers to feed on. Many animals occupy more than one trophic level because they will feed on both plants and/or different sorts of animals depending on what is available.

The system of trophic levels applies only as long as the organism being consumed is alive and whole. Dead organisms or the waste products from living ones are also part of the food web and are consumed by **scavengers** (large animals which feed on dead remains), **detritovores** (small animals which feed on dead remains) and a whole range of **micro-organisms** which are aso referred to as **decomposers**. Furthermore, **parasites** which live in or on other living organisms are not generally included in trophic levels.

Autotrophs include plants and chemo-autotrophic bacteria. Both groups of organisms produce their own organic molecules using simple molecules (e.g. carbon dioxide, water) and an energy source such as the sun or other molecules (e.g. methane, hydrogen sulphide). **Heterotrophs** feed on autotrophs from which they derive complex organic molecules.

energy flow

In the great majority of food chains and webs the original source of energy is the Sun. **Energy flow** through food chains and webs describes the way energy passes from the Sun through the different trophic levels. Energy is stored in organisms in the form of body material, which is consumed by an organism at the next trophic level to be converted into body material and so on. At each trophic level energy is lost in heat, movement, sometimes in the production of sound and more rarely of light or electricity. The greater part of available energy at each level is lost in this way. This is the factor that limits the number of possible trophic levels. Beyond four the consumer would generally have to expend more energy finding food than would be available for effective living and growth.

In food chains or webs the energy flow is represented by arrows which always point away from the organism (or, in the case of plants, the Sun) which is providing the energy. Often the width of the arrow is used to illustrate the amount of energy flowing from one trophic level to the next.

Figure 8.1
Energy flow through a food chain or web.

Note that although biologists refer to energy 'flow', physicists refer to energy *change*. Energy is not a fluid and cannot flow.

pyramids of numbers

These are simply graphical illustrations of how different quantities (e.g. numbers of organisms, their mass, their energy) vary up the trophic levels in an ecosystem. They are called pyramids because the typical picture is pyramid-shaped, but not all are. Pyramids can be mathematically precise if quantities are known, but can still be useful even without such precision.

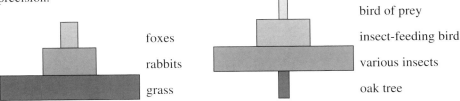

Figure 8.2
Two examples of pyramids of numbers.

growth curves

Population growth over time can be illustrated on growth curve graphs.

There are two important examples:

The **S-shaped** growth curve is produced where a population starts to grow slowly at first but more rapidly with time. After a while, however, the rate of growth slows due to limiting factors in the environment. Eventually the population stops increasing in size (i.e. death rate = birth rate) and the curve reaches a plateau.

The **J-shaped** growth curve essentially follows the S-shaped one in the initial stages but its growth rate does not slow with time. The population continues to grow rapidly producing an almost vertical line on the graph. Such population growth must stop eventually; sometimes in a catastrophic manner. This is illustrated by the fatal infection of an organism by a micro-organism whose numbers increase rapidly until the host is killed – when the micro-organisms must die too, apart from reproductive spores.

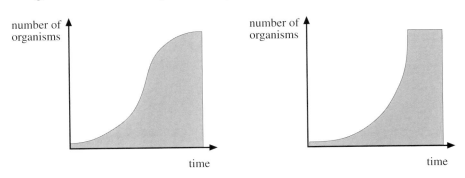

Figure 8.3
a An S-shaped growth curve.   **b** A J-shaped growth curve.

Population growth is influenced by different factors. The effects of **density-dependent factors** change as the population size changes. Such factors include the amount of space available and competition between organisms. **Density-independent factors** do *not* vary with population size and include climate and (depending on circumstances) water. Nutrients for plants may be density-independent.

population sampling

A study of ecology requires that the numbers of organisms in an ecosystem be known. Since it is generally impossible to count every organism, some form of **sample** must be taken from which the whole population size can be estimated. For the study of population changes over time changes to the sample size may provide sufficient information.

Sampling requires the observer to define an area and count all the chosen organisms in that area. There are many ways of doing this.

A **quadrat** is a square frame (often 1 metre square) which is placed randomly over a site so that the number of quadrats equates to 5–10% of the site area.

A **line transect** is a string drawn across the site. Samples can then be taken at fixed intervals along the line either simply seeing what is under the line or using a **point frame**.

A **belt transect** is similar to a point transect but the samples are taken using a quadrat at fixed intervals. Random quadrats allow a simple survey of an area. Transects can be used to identify changes in animals or plants over distance such as from the water's edge to the top of a seashore.

These methods work well for plants or sedentary animals. For most animals some method of capturing them must be used. Examples of these include:

- **sweep net**, sweeping a net through vegetation or water;

- **kick sampling** in a river – kicking the river bottom just in front of a net so that any animals disturbed are swept into the net;

- **beating** a plant or tree to shake the animals off on to a collecting sheet; using a **pooter** to suck small animals off the collecting sheet or directly off vegetation;

- **pitfall traps**, where animals fall into a simple container on the ground and cannot escape;

- **sticky traps**, used on tree trunks, which generally kill the animals.

capture-recapture

One way of estimating the size of an animal population is to capture a sample, mark the individuals in some indelible way and release them back into their habitat. Some time later capture a second sample and count the number of marked and unmarked individuals. The population size can be estimated using the formula:

$$\text{population size} = \frac{\text{number first caught and marked} \times \text{total caught second time}}{\text{number of marked individuals in second catch}}$$

This method works only if the population is contained, with no immigration or emigration; there are no appreciable births or deaths over the sampling period; the marking has no effect on the animal or its chance of being recaptured and if marked animals mix freely with the rest of the population.

abundance

Just as pyramids are used to produce a picture of organisms at trophic levels, other diagrams are used to illustrate the abundance of organisms in an ecosystem. Sampling produces numbers which can be converted into simple **histograms** or **abundance diagrams** (sometimes also called **kite diagrams**). The latter are most useful when illustrating changes in population numbers over distance or time. The width of each band represents the relative abundance of each organism. (See also Section 11.4.)

Figure 8.4
Abundance diagram showing how the numbers of individuals of four different species change over distance; the width of each 'kite' indicates relative abundance.

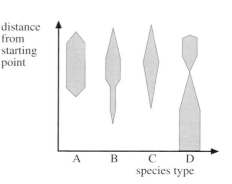

eutrophication	**Eutrophication** is the state resulting when large algal growths (perhaps brought about by high quantities of nitrates in the water) eventually die and are decomposed by bacteria. In doing this the bacteria use up most of the available oxygen (and produce H_2S) which kills fish, etc. **Oligotrophic** describes water which is low in ions and organic matter.
nutrient cycling	**Nutrient cycling** is the movement of essential elements between trophic levels and between organisms and the soil, water or air. The elements are not lost but continuously cycle among living organisms and their physical environment. Generally such organisms also move between ecosystems, making it more difficult to trace or predict their movement.

8.2M.2 Genetics

genetic material	The simplest building blocks for genetic material are **nucleotides**. These are molecules made up of a pentose sugar (either ribose or deoxyribose), a phosphate group and an organic base. Nucleotides are joined into long chains (polynucleotides) by an addition-elimination ('condensation') reaction between the phosphate group of one nucleotide and the pentose group of another. The organic bases are not involved in the chain formation so 'stick out' at intervals along the chain and can join to the bases in a second chain by hydrogen bonding, forming DNA (DeoxyriboNucleic Acid).

The bases are **adenine**, **cytosine**, **guanine** and **thymine** in the DNA molecule: in RNA thymine is replaced by **uracil.** When a pair of polynucleotide chains join together adenine forms hydrogen bonds always with thymine and cytosine with guanine.

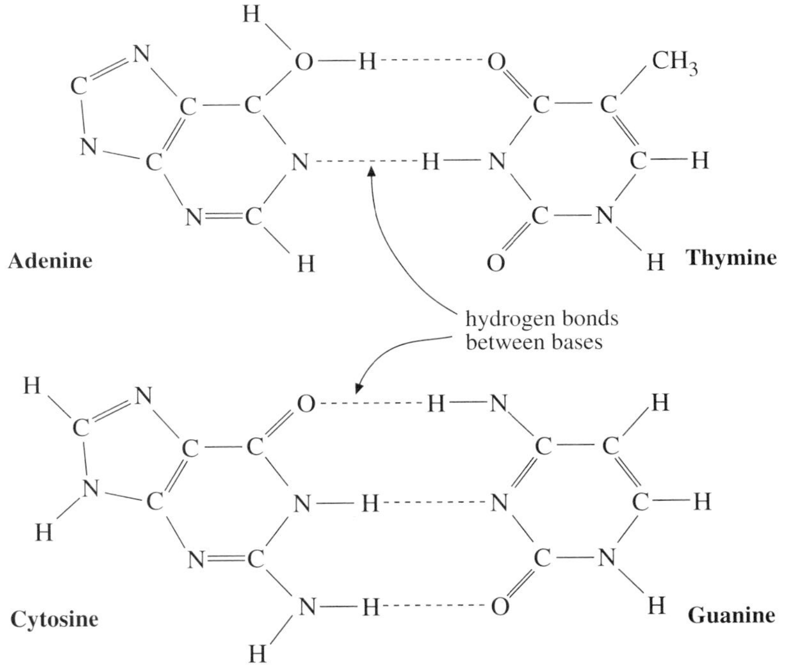

Figure 8.5
Hydrogen bonding between bases.

The DNA molecule, therefore, consists of two parallel long chains, joined together at intervals by hydrogen bonds between the bases rather like the rungs of a ladder. This structure can become twisted into the shape of a helix (hence the term 'The Double Helix') and further coiled to shorten (and fatten) the molecule. In order to function correctly, though, the molecule must to some extent untwist.

Replication is the process by which DNA molecules reproduce themselves exactly during cell reproduction. The ladder structure is essential to this process because the DNA molecule splits down the middle with each chain rebuilding its own parallel opposite chain.

RNA (RiboNucleic Acid) exists as a single chain of nucleotides. The organic bases simply stick out of the side of the molecule without pairing to another. Adenine is still capable, however, of pairing with guanine and uracil with cytosine.

genes	DNA carries genetic information in the nucleus of the cell (or free, in the cell of Prokaryotes). A **gene** is a sequence of DNA bases which carries enough information for the construction of one polypeptide (or in the case of smaller proteins, for the whole protein).

8   **Glossary**

Proteins are made from building blocks called **amino acids**. Only 20 different sorts of amino acids occur naturally; proteins vary in the number and sequence of the amino acids they contain. Within the DNA molecule the organic bases are functionally organised into groups of three, called **triplets**. Different triplets, (e.g.AAA or ACT) are the code for different amino acids. Thus, sections of DNA contain the code for the number and sequence of amino acids in different proteins. **Introns** are interrupters found within an gene (and considered part of it) which are transcribed (see below) and later spliced out of the complete m-RNA (Messenger RNA) to leave only the exons.

genome   **Genome** is the total gene complement of an organism.

genetic fingerprinting   This is a somewhat inaccurate term used to describe the analysis by electrophoresis of a sample of DNA. The DNA is purified and then cut into short lengths using restriction enzymes. These are then separated by electrophoresis on the basis of their size but are at this stage invisible. The invisible pattern is transferred on to a nylon membrane which is then flooded with radioactive DNA probes. These adhere to the DNA pattern on the membrane and allow a picture to be produced on photographic film.

transcription   **Transcription** is a process whereby the code in DNA is converted into a strand of m-RNA (Messenger RNA). In a typical cell nucleus free RNA nucleotides are joined together to form a strand of m-RNA according to the code specified in a section of DNA. The DNA triplet when it is transcribed into m-RNA is then called a **codon**.

translation   **Translation** is the process whereby the information in m-RNA is used to construct a protein. Molecules of t-RNA (Transfer RNA) exist freely in the cell and different sorts combine with the different amino acid molecules which also exist in cells. Each of the different t-RNA molecules has at one site an exposed triplet called an **anticodon** which is the mirror-image of a codon. m-RNA from the nucleus attaches to a section of RNA on a ribosome in the cell. t-RNA with its amino acid attaches itself, via the codon-anticodon link, to the m-RNA and then enzymes in the ribosomes join neighbouring amino acids to form the protein.

polysome   A **polysome** is a single strand of m-RNA which is attached to several ribosomes at the same time all constructing the same polypeptide but at different stages of construction.

sense and nonsense strands   In transcription only one side (or strand) of the DNA ladder is actually a working code. It is sometimes called the sense strand. The opposite side of the ladder carries no sensible genetic code and is therefore a nonsense strand.

genetic modification   **Genetic modification** (also commonly, but less accurately, known as **gene manipulation** or **genetic engineering**) is the alteration of the DNA of an organism by inserting short lengths of DNA from other organisms into it. Such DNA, if it does not exist naturally, is called **recombinant DNA**.

Prokaryote (bacterial) cells have no nucleus; their DNA exists as a long ring in the cell with the addition of smaller rings of DNA called **plasmids**. **Restriction enzymes** which occur naturally in bacteria can be isolated and artificially used to cut up donor DNA into short sections or to open up plasmid rings. **Ligase** is an enzyme which enables cut ends of DNA to re-join, a process called **annealing**. Recombinant DNA plasmids can be constructed using donor DNA, bacterial plasmids and ligase. They can be inserted in bacteria (often the same sort of bacteria that the plasmids came from) by immersing the bacterial culture in a mixture that contains the plasmids. Applying a brief electric shock causes minute temporary holes to open up in the cell membrane through which the plasmids can pass – a process called **electroporation**.

Using restriction enzymes and ligase, human genes such as that for the production of insulin have been inserted into bacterial cells which then produce large quantities of insulin and the DNA which codes for it.

Recombinant DNA plasmids have been introduced into plant cells but not really successfully into mammalian cells. The genomes of higher organisms are much more complex than those of bacteria and complete **gene expression** generally requires more than simply the addition of a new gene. Current research is attempting to insert lengths of recombinant DNA into egg cell nuclei where they are more likely to become incorporated into the genome of the new animal.

cloning   **Cloning** is the creation of one or more genetically identical organisms from a single donor organism. In plants the process generally involves the separation of single cells which are

122

then grown into complete organisms initially on a specialised growth medium. Successful mammalian cloning ('Dolly', the sheep) used a cell which was inserted into the uterus of a surrogate mother sheep, which then grew in the same way as a normal embryo.

gene therapy

Gene therapy is the strategy of treating genetically-caused diseases by the replacement of defective genes by healthy ones. This is at an early stage of development and at present workers are concentrating on bone marrow, liver and skin cells because these cells divide and replicate easily in the body.

linked genes

Linkage applies to genes which are found on the same chromosome. Generally therefore they always express themselves together. Some famous examples include that for haemophilia, found on the human female (X) chromosome. In males with only one X chromosome, whatever gene is part of that chromosome will be expressed. Thus haemophilia usually affects only males since the gene is recessive and uncommon, and any females will be likely to have a gene on the other X chromosome for normal blood clotting. Genes on the sex chromosomes are called **sex-linked. Autosomal linkage** is the name given to linkage between genes on chromosomes other than the sex chromosomes.

Crossing over describes a process during meiosis as the four chromatids in any homologous pair shorten and untwine. Breaks in individual chromatids occur and are repaired but sometimes parts of opposite chromatids become joined. New mixes of genes are produced on individual chromatids. Crossing over has the potential to alter linkage. The **cross-over value** has been shown to remain fairly constant for different pairs of genes and is larger the further apart the genes are on the chromosome. The cross-over value is given by the formula:

$$\frac{\text{number of recombinant individual offspring produced}}{\text{total number of offspring produced}} \times 100$$

more terms in genetics

A **homologous pair** is the two chromosomes, one from each parent, which correspond with each other in terms of size, the number of genes they carry and the features these genes code for. Homologous chromosomes are not identical since the genes they carry may lead to different characteristics in the same feature (e.g. the ability or inability to roll the tongue). Pairs of genes like this are known as **alleles**. In such pairs one gene may be **dominant**, i.e. it is always expressed; **recessive**, i.e. its expression is masked by a dominant allele; or the two alleles may be **co-dominant**.

Chromatids is a word used to describe parts of a chromosome visible just before and during meiosis and mitosis. Students sometimes confuse chromatids with homologous pairs. Prior to meiosis or mitosis each chromosome undergoes replication to become two identical chromosomes joined at some point. They appear and are often drawn as a sort of X-shaped structure. Homologous pairs are visible as pairs of X-shaped structures. Confusion arises with the location of alleles on the homologous pairs. Students sometimes believe the alleles to be the pair of genes on the two joined chromatids which of course is wrong since these genes are identical, having been produced from the single original chromosome by replication.

Mitosis is the division of a cell into two new cells each with exactly the same genome as each other and the parent cell. Mitosis is the cell division which occurs as a part of growth.

Meiosis is the division of a reproductive cell into four new cells which have half the genome of the parent cell. Generally the four new cells (also known as **gametes**) are two pairs each with the same genes, but if crossing over occurs all four new cells will have a different gene complement. A typical cell has two sets of chromosomes, each set containing one of each homologous pair. Cells like this, with a full genome, are called **diploid**. Cells with only one set of chromosomes are called **haploid**. Sometimes plant cells can, naturally or artificially, achieve more than two sets of chromosomes. Those with three are called **triploid**.

life cycles

A **diplontic** life cycle describes the common life cycle found in plants and animals whereby the cells of the organism are diploid for the great majority of the life cycle other than the reproductive gametes. A **haplontic** life cycle describes a condition whereby meiosis occurs immediately after fertilisation leading to haploid cells which form the body of the organism. Spirogyra is an example of an organism with a haplontic life cycle. **Haplo-diplontic** is used to describe the life cycle of organisms (plants) which exhibit alternation of generations, one being haploid and the next diploid. Mosses and liverworts are haplodiplontic, but the condition can be traced in all green plants in one form or another.

mutation	Mutations occur naturally and randomly, but can also be artificially induced by drugs or radiation (mutagens). In a **point mutation** a single base change has a significant effect, e.g. in sickle cell anaemia. In **frameshift mutations** the addition or deletion of bases alters the sequence of triplets. A **chromosome aberration** may be addition or deletion of a whole chromosome or a part of one. This is called **aneuploidy** and the best-known example is perhaps Down's Syndrome (one extra chromosome). Altering the number of whole sets of chromosomes is called **euploidy**. Having three or more sets of chromosomes is called **polyeuploidy**. This may arise from some failure of cell division in which case all the chromosomes come from the same species – **autoploid**. When some chromosomes come from another species the condition is labelled **allopolyploid**. Modern wheat is derived from a plant which was a naturally-occurring allopolyploid. Most cultivated crops are polyploids.
Hardy–Weinberg principle	This states that in a large and randomly-mating population the gene and genotype frequencies remain constant. This principle can be used to calculate the frequency of a recessive gene if the frequency of the genotype is known. Mathematically the principle is explained by two equations, where p is the frequency of one allele and q the frequency of the other. p^2 is the frequency of the homozygous dominant and $2pq$ the frequency of the heterozygous dominant but, most importantly, q^2 is the frequency of the homozygous recessive which is likely to be the genotype most easily identified. $$p + q = 1$$ $$p^2 + 2pq + q^2 = 1$$ The principle can also be used to identify whether a population remains large and randomly-mating or whether some factor is at work changing the **gene pool**.
genetic drift	**Genetic drift** is the alteration to the gene pool of a population because of the persistent presence of one or more biotic or abiotic factors in the environment which kill large numbers of the population. Those that remain breed to form succeeding generations but inevitably they have less variation in their gene pool to pass on. If the environmental factors persist for a long time the population produced will become very specialised. Genetic drift and **natural selection** operate in the same way. Genetic drift is generally used to describe less-pronounced changes in the gene pool than natural selection.

8.2M.3 Miscellaneous

species	See 9.2G, 9.2M and 9.2N
water potential	See 9.2M

8.2N Earth science

age: absolute	The age of a rock, fossil, mineral, structure, etc., in years or millions of years (commonly obtained by isotopes (radiometric dating)).
age: relative	The position of a rock, etc., in a time sequence – often the age in years or millions of years (the 'absolute age') is not known.
acidic	See 9.2G and 9.2N
acme	The geological time when the phylum referred to shows its greatest variety of species.
aggregate	Refers to broken or crushed stone of differing sizes used in the construction industry.
amplitude	See 9.2B and 9.2N
anomaly	The case in which a measured distribution or physical phenomenon is greater or less than the average background value, e.g. magnetic anomaly.
association	See 9.2N
asthenosphere	See 9.2N
atomic structure	See 9.2N
average crustal abundance	The percentage of an element in the Earth's crust. Data may be given for the whole Earth's crust or for the Continental crust only.
basic	See 9.2G and 9.2N
cement	See 9.2N
cementation	See 9.2H and 9.2N

cleavage	See 9.2N
competency	Refers to a rigid rock unit that tends to resist plastic deformation. An **incompetent** rock may flow under stress, e.g. clay.
confining pressure	Pressure exerted by the surrounding rock load.
contamination	Additions to the chemistry of an igneous rock due to its ability to remove or 'leach' materials from the surrounding country rocks whilst in the molten state.
correlation	See 9.2N
cumulate	An igneous rock or mineral deposit which owes its texture and chemical content to the setting of heavier minerals under the influence of gravity where they accumulate at the base of a melt.
cut-off grade	The minimum percentage of an element in a mineral that can be worked profitably.
declination	The angle that Magnetic North makes with respect to Geographic North. Inclination is the angle a dip needle takes measured to the horizontal. (A dip needle is a magnetic needle that can rotate only in a vertical plane.) Magnetic inclination at the magnetic poles is 90° and at the equator is 0°. The method can be used to find the latitude of formation of rock samples.
derived	A fossil or clast, a rock fragment or a broken mineral, weathered from its original site and redeposited in a later horizon.
diagenesis	See 9.2N
differentiation	The separation of a melt into distinct chemical associations or 'fractions' under the effect of time, heat and gravity. Should the fractions crystallize out the resulting different rock types may be described as due to **magmatic segregation**.
discontinuity	A change of state forming an interface between distinct physical units: commonly related to changes in the structure of the Earth with depth.
earthquake intensity	Measured on the Mercalli scale: a measure of destructive force obtained by plotting levels of observed surface damage after the event. See 3.2N.9.
earthquake magnitude	Measured on the Richter scale: a measure of the energy released by the event. See 3.2N.10.
effusive eruption	Eruption of highly fluid lavas at high temperature, containing large quantities of dissolved gas causing high energy eruption as the gases escape with, sometimes, spectacular fire fountains.
eustatic change	A change in sea level: e.g. caused by the melting of ice sheets. **Isostatic** is the effect of depressing the land surface by added weight. **Isostatic rebound** occurs when the weight is removed and the land surface adjusts by rising.
evaporites	The result of dissolved salts crystallizing out and forming sedimentary layers due to the evaporation of confined or semi-confined bodies of water.
facies	An association of fossils and rock texture indicating a specific environment of deposition. May also be used to describe the relationship between rock texture and index minerals in a metamorphic environment.
fluid pressure	In metamorphism: pressure exerted by fluids in rock pores.
foliation	'Sheet-like'; a layering effect in rocks caused by pressure in metamorphic environments. **Lineation** describes the orientation of minerals in a metamorphic rock due to directional stress.
flocculation	The process in which charged colloidal particles such as clays, having the ability to bind together by electrostatic attraction, aggregate themselves into larger particles which then settle out of the water.
geothermal energy	The energy obtained from the harnessing (by heat exchange systems) of geysers, hot springs or areas of active volcanism or magma intrusion, in regions of high hydrothermal activity.
geothermal gradient	The rate at which temperature increases with depth from the Earth's surface. It has significant geographical variation, being greater in areas of high heat flow and less in cooler areas.
grade	See 9.2N
habit	See 9.2N
half-life	See 8.2A

hardness	See 9.2H and 9.2N
hot spot	See 9.2N
hydrothermal ores	Ores resulting from the selective crystallisation of minerals from hot aqueous solutions circulating through joints, fissures and weaknesses in the rocks. Commonly thought to originate in igneous environments but study shows that such solutions can sometimes have a sedimentary origin. The term may be subdivided by measurements of the range of temperature involved.
index mineral	A mineral of which the conditions of formation, in terms of temperature and pressure, are confirmed by laboratory investigation. Therefore its presence in rocks indicates the range of conditions under which the whole rock may have been formed.
intermediate	See 9.2G and 9.2N
ionic substitution	See 9.2N
life/death assemblages	See 9.2N
lithosphere	See 9.2N
maturity	See 9.2N
mineral	A naturally-occurring solid element or compound with predictable physical properties.
ore	A material of value that can be worked profitably. Though commonly applied to minerals it can, in theory, refer to any geological material.
orogeny, orogenesis	A period in geological time when mountain building was significant due to plate movement (tectonic collision). Also used as a noun: e.g. alpine orogeny.
palaeoenvironment	An environment of the geological past. **Palaeo-** as 'geologically old'; e.g. palaeogeography, palaeontology.
plastic	See 9.2G and 9.2N
punctuated equilibrium	The pulse-like arrival of new species which do not appear to have evolved directly from the steady biota in that place. Explained by their evolution in isolated areas and then a geologically 'sudden' migration into the record.
pyroclastic flow	A violent density current of ash, broken rock, gases and lava 'bombs' expelled at a high temperature, 1000 °C, and with great force from an explosive eruption. Moves at speed down slope under the influence of gravity.
reserve	A proven resource that can be extracted commercially under the prevailing economic conditions.
resources	All known and conjectured occurrences of an economic material including those that are not economic to exploit under the present conditions.
sial	An old term, still found, referring to the continental crust, as it is dominated by oxides of silicon and aluminium. **Sima** refers to the oceanic crust, dominated by oxides of silicon and magnesium. The '**crust**' is the thin upper rigid layer of the lithosphere. Both sial and sima are serious oversimplifications of crustal chemistry.
sima	[included above]
solid solution	See 9.2G and 9.2N
species	See 9.2G, 9.2M and 9.2N
stability fields	See 9.2N
suture	See 9.2N
terrestrial	See 9.2N
texture	See 9.2N
Uniformitarianism	See 9.2N
vagrant	Used to describe the life-style of creatures that are mobile on the sea floor or lake bed, rather than swimming (e.g. crab) or burrowing (e.g. cockles).
volatiles	See 9.2G and 9.2N
zone fossil	See 9.2N

9 MINEFIELD

9.1 Introduction

Chapter 9 and Chapter 8 ('Glossary') are complementary.

The Glossary is targeted at those teachers who are teaching just inside – or sometimes just outside – the limits of their specialist knowledge. The Working Party is here thinking of the chemist teaching the Soil Science or Biochemistry options at A-level, the geologist the former, and the physicist or chemist coping with aspects of Materials. Such teachers might welcome some guidance with technical terms.

The Minefield is written for those specialists who have perhaps become over-familiar with their subject and as a result have begun to use words loosely or over-simply or ambiguously or even wrongly. Of course none of those reading this book think that this would apply to them! Nevertheless at least two of the Working Party confess to fallibility on these lines. It is hoped therefore that this chapter will be thought-provoking and useful for all those who dip into it.

In Chapters 8 and 9 the sequence is that of the topics listed in Chapter 2; items are usually arranged alphabetically within each topic. Where a word is used with a different meaning in another branch of science, it is cross-referred to the appropriate sub-section (e.g. 'see 9.2G'). Items in this chapter are not cross-referred back to the Glossary.

Sub-sections in which there is at the moment no entry are still listed.

9.2A Length and time
9.2B Motion, mass and force

action/reaction	These are highly misleading words. At the very least they imply cause and effect; at worst they imply a wilful aggressor and its (unsuspecting) target – even between inanimate objects. A time delay is often inferred. See also Newton's Third Law, 9.2B below.
amplitude	The maximum displacement of an oscillation from the mean. See 9.2N.
centrifugal/centripetal forces	'Centrifugal' means 'away from the centre' and 'centripetal' means 'towards the centre'. Both of these names can be given (legitimately) to the same effect but the choice will depend upon the viewpoint ('frame of reference', see 9.2B below) of the observer. A teddy bear in a spin drier might tell you that he is being pushed against the outside of the drum by a strong force: to him the force is 'centrifugal'. You, however, recognise that were it not for the wall of the drum the toy would fly off at a tangent in a straight line (apart from the effect of gravity) so you recognise the force of the drum wall upon the bear only *towards the centre*. In other words you recognise only a 'centripetal' force. In about 1960 there was international agreement that pupils while at school would be taught to analyse problems only in terms of centripetal force. In other words the pupils would be taught to imagine themselves as standing *outside* the rotating system (even if they were inside it). The teddy bears of this world, and most of their owners, find it difficult to imagine themselves in a frame of reference other than their own. But it is worth their effort to stay, in imagination, in the 'outside' frame of reference and to argue in terms of 'centripetal' force *while analysing rotational motion*.

force diagrams

When illustrating the forces upon a body, the body should be drawn in isolation, as shown in Figure 9.1 for the example of someone pushing a pram so that it accelerates.

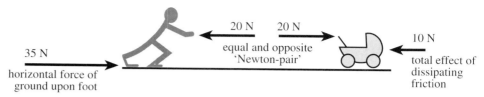

Figure 9.1
Illustrating the forces on a body.

frame of reference

This is the 'frame' (position or ground) from which you view something that is happening. While analysing any form of motion it is vital that you recognise the frame from which you are viewing it in your imagination – *and stay in that frame*. An example of what happens when we fail to recognise our frame of reference is the mistake many authors make over the action of the calf-muscle: they argue (incorrectly) that when your heels are just off the ground the calf-muscle is 'advantaged' whereas the calf-muscles are in truth severely 'disadvantaged', having to exert a force about ten times as great as the value usually arrived at in such texts. Here is a case where it pays to imagine yourself part of the moving system instead of 'standing outside it'. A similar mistake is sometimes made about rowing. (See centrifugal/centripetal forces, 9.2B, fulcrum/pivot, 9.2B, and levers, 9.2B.)

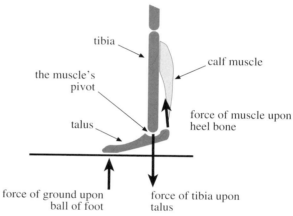

Figure 9.2
Frame of reference.

friction/grip

Friction is the force experienced by each of two 'bodies', equally, as they move past each other, *or attempt to do so*. If there is 'slip' then their surfaces become hotter; if there is purely 'grip' there can be no transfer of energy between the bodies themselves. However, a tyre rolling without slipping on the road does become hotter. This is because there is slip between the particles within the tyre itself, as the tyre changes shape while it rolls.

fulcrum/pivot

These are conventionally synonymous, but it would be helpful to redefine them as follows:

Fulcrum: 'the point upon which no work is done'.

Pivot: 'the point about which a lever is made to rotate from within the pivot's own frame of reference'.

levers

There have been traditionally three classes of levers, named according to the relative positions of the Load, the Effort and the Fulcrum.

1st class: the fulcrum is between the effort and the load, e.g. a seesaw.

2nd class: the load is between the effort and the fulcrum, e.g. a wheelbarrow.

3rd class: the effort is between the load and the fulcrum, e.g. sugar tongs.

One of the Working Party has united the concepts of frame of reference, fulcrum/pivot and levers into this account of a 'self-propelled assault machine' shown in the box opposite.

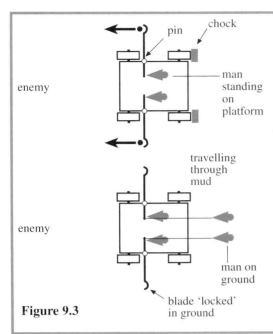

pin   chock

enemy

man standing on platform

travelling through mud

enemy

man on ground

blade 'locked' in ground

Figure 9.3

(a) With the machine fixed in place stones are flicked at the enemy. (Reloaders not shown.) The fulcrum is at the pin and all the men's energy output is transferred to the projectiles. For escape, the chocks are removed and the machine retreats, still flicking stones but more slowly, since some of the men's output energy goes on propelling the machine. The fulcrum *is now that point on the oar which does not move relative to the ground*. In order to transfer all their output energy into propulsion of the machine the men would have to 'lock' the ends of the oars firmly into the ground – thick mud, perhaps – and the fulcrum would be at the end of the blade.

(b) Wherever the fulcrum might be, each man's pivot would always be at his pin. If 'ground staff' gave some help by pulling on the oar handles with ropes, as shown, while men were 'rowing' through the mud, then because they would be standing on the ground *their* pivots would be at the blades.

momentum

The momentum of a particle is defined as 'its mass × its velocity'. When 'mass × velocity' was found to be a profoundly important quantity it had to be given a label. The label chosen was the word 'momentum'.

Why is 'mass × velocity' important? It stems from the fundamentally important fact that the motion of the centre of mass of a system of particles is not *directly* affected by any interaction between those particles. That's all; but it is more commonly known in the form of its corollary 'The total momentum of any system of particles is not altered as a direct result of any interaction between these particles'.

Unfortunately, convention has us saying 'The total momentum of ... *is conserved*'; whereas we would do better using the words 'The total momentum of ... *remains constant*'. By using 'constancy' in the context of momentum and using 'conservation' *only* when talking about 'energy' we would make it less easy for students to get the subconscious idea that 'momentum' and 'energy' are 'the same sort of thing'.

Newton's Third Law

If body A experiences a force there is always another body B which experiences a force of equal magnitude acting in the opposite direction.

Newton's Third Law is always to do with **two** bodies. The equal and opposite forces acting upon the two bodies are sometimes called a 'Newton-pair' (Figure 9.1). (Newton's First and Second Laws are to do with ONE body only.) See action/reaction, 9.2B.

Caution: Use 'while' rather than 'when'. 'When I hit him, he always hits me back.' 'While I push on him he pushes back on me with an equal and opposite force.' If we say 'when I push on him he pushes back on me....' it is ambiguous. The use of 'when' suggests cause and effect or even, perhaps subconsciously, a time-delay. See action/reaction, 9.2B.

tension/compression

'Tension' and 'compression' are *conditions,* not forces. We talk about the 'tension in a guitar string' but mean 'a guitar string under tension'. Two forces produce the tension in the string: one at each end, pulling in opposite directions. A snake can be killed by subjecting it to sufficient tension: either by holding it at head and tail and stretching it, or by holding its tail and 'flicking' it like a whip. In the latter case there is only one external force acting upon the snake (apart from its weight, of course, of little significance here), and the tension within the snake will not be uniform. Similarly, a rugby-playing pilot can have his spine dangerously compressed either in a static scrum or by ejecting from his aircraft.

speed/velocity of light

The speed of light in a vacuum is 3×10^8 m s^{-1}, or more properly 300×10^6 m s^{-1}. This is commonly (but incorrectly) referred to as its velocity.

People say 'light travels in straight lines', in which case 'velocity' is implied. But the conditions under which light travels in a straight line are special (in a vacuum, with no gravitational field, etc.) so the word 'speed' here is acceptable and most books use it. When quoting the '*velocity*' of something, the *direction* should be specified as well as the magnitude. If only the *magnitude* is given we are quoting a *speed*.

weight	'Weight' is given a greater variety of meanings than any other word (and often in the same paragraph!). It is because this fact is not recognised, (or if recognised, often suppressed) that the word 'weight' causes so much confusion.

Meanings in common use include:

'The gravitational force (upon a body)'.

'The resultant force (in a vacuum) which gives a body its measured gravitational acceleration'.

'The gravitational force acting upon a body when the body is in equilibrium'.

'The force with which a body pushes down upon a supporting surface'.

'The upward force of the supporting surface'.

'A standard lump of metal used when 'weighing' with scales'.

(Which of these would the reader use/reject?) We read about scientists conducting experiments in the free fall of an orbiting space station in order to simulate 'zero-gravity', or in the vertical fall of a mini-lab through the higher atmosphere in order to simulate 'micro-gravity'.

The majority of texts use 'weight (of)' to mean 'the force of gravity (upon)'.

weightlessness	Its meaning depends on your meaning of 'weight'. Beware of using 'weightlessness' when you mean '*feeling* weightless'. Beware also of even talking about 'feeling weightless!'

9.2C   Changing direction

9.2D   Energy

energy transfer diagrams	A diagram of the route along which energy is transmitted (and transferred). The type of diagram chosen must be appropriate, and correctly labelled.

Notes:
(a) Any device travelling or operating at constant speed has constant energy, so the only energy transferred *in* that device goes to increase the energy of the environment (as wasted 'heat'). The rest of the energy received by the device is transmitted on to the next device in the chain. For example, once an 'electric power' transmission system is running at virtually constant speed its energy transfer diagram should not show any change in the energy of each device in the chain. An example of this is a water turbine charging a battery.

(b) When energy is transferred in a series of separate stages, some of the transfers will, of course, be in series; but there are other transfers in parallel as well. For example, when a boy slams a door shut by pushing it with his foot there are three sets of transfers in parallel:

  (i)   Chemical energy → KE of door → increase in internal energy of house

  (ii) Chemical energy → KE of leg → increase in internal energy of leg

  (iii) Chemical energy → increase in internal energy of whole body (due to its inefficiency)

(c) It is *wrong* to say 'Chemical energy → KE of leg → KE of door → increase in internal energy of house' (unless the boy took off his false leg and threw it at the door). This is a common textbook error.

transfer/transform	Energy *transfer* is a process which occurs with or without transformation. *Transform* is used inconsistently by physicists. It accurately describes what happens when energy changes its manifestation ('form') when it is 'transferred' but we are now frightened to use the word, even when it is appropriate. We use the word *inappropriately,* however, when labelling the electro-magnetic gearing device comonly called a 'transformer'. The so-called 'transformer' does not trans-form at all. Like any gearing system it matches the 'source' to the 'load' – so should be called a 'gear'. The simplest mechanical equivalent is the lever, in the form of the oar. The loudspeaker is an example of a 'true' transformer, converting electrical energy to sound and heat energy.

9.2E Heat

'heat' used as a noun	Frowned upon, except perhaps when defined as 'heat is energy in transit as a result of a temperature difference'. But note that once the energy has arrived you may no longer call it 'heat'! It becomes 'increase in internal energy of...' More precisely, the heat will not only raise the internal energy of the body which absorbed it but also cause the body to expand. This expansion causes work to be done in raising the centre of gravity and work to be done against atmospheric pressure (and see the comment on enthalpy below). **Comment**: We need to tread carefully between extreme rigour – which may confuse younger students – and not being rigorous enough, which may spoil for older students some of the fascinating subtleties of physics. It is hard to be rigidly correct when faced with anachronisms such as 'specific heat capacity'!
'heat' used as a verb	Physics teachers are nervous of using this word. It is all right to use it as a verb, as in 'heating water', but a body can be heated only as result of a temperature difference. It is correct to say 'water was heated in the kettle' if it gained the energy because the water was cooler than the hot element, but if you were to raise the temperature of the water by hurling the kettle at a brick wall you should not claim to have 'heated' it. First you gave the whole mass KE as a travelling 'lump'; then, upon crashing, the KE becomes transferred as an increase in its internal energy. The average (random) KE of the molecules increases. To play safe use 'I raised its temperature' or 'I made it hotter' whatever method of hotting-up you employed. To make matters worse: unless the kettle is hermetically sealed and does not change in volume it is its *enthalpy*, see 8.2E, that has changed, rather than its *internal energy*! Chemists instinctively think in terms of glass apparatus, open to the atmosphere – physicists don't.

9.2F Molecular properties

amount of substance	In ordinary life the word 'amount' can be applied to a mass or a volume or a number as well as having specialist meanings as, for example, here. In a chemical context the word should be used only when the answer to the question 'What amount of it?' is 'x mol of it'. Until recently no name was uniformly given to the quantity whose unit is the 'mole'. The name 'amount of substance' is now reserved for this quantity by international agreement. It is correct, for example, to state '$n(Na) = 0.1$ mol, where $n(Na)$ denotes the amount of substance of Na', whilst it is incorrect to refer to '$n(Na)$, the number of moles of sodium' since n is a symbol for a physical quantity, not for a number. In the same way it would be incorrect to refer to '$m(Na)$, the number of kilograms of sodium' but correct to state '$m(Na) = 2.3$ kg, where $m(Na)$ denotes the mass of sodium'. The amount of substance is *proportional to* the number of specified elementary entities of that substance. The proportionality factor is the same for all substances; its reciprocal is L, the Avogadro constant [$(6.022\,045 \pm 0.000\,031) \times 10^{23}$ mol^{-1}]. Note that the Avogadro constant is a physical quantity with the dimension (amount-of-substance)$^{-1}$, and is not a pure number. **The term 'Avogadro number' should not be used.** The specified entity may be an atom, a molecule, an ion, a radical, an electron, an equation, etc., or any *specified* group of particles whether or not the specified group has any real separate existence. Examples include a mole of NaCl(s), a mole of C–C bonds or a mole of the reaction represented by the equation ($N_2O_4 \rightleftharpoons 2NO_2$). For the last example the phrase 'a mole of the reaction $N_2O_4 \rightleftharpoons 2NO_2$' may be a convenient term. **It is essential to quote a symbol or formula rather than use a name alone** in statements of this kind because there can be confusion over the entity involved, e.g. mercury(I) chloride, sulfur, iodine, ethanoic acid. Thus to refer to '1.5 mol of sulfur' would be incorrect because it would be meaningless. Even '1.5 mol of sulfur molecules' would be ambiguous as the molecules might be S_2, S_8, etc. Similarly, '2 moles of nitrogen dioxide molecules' is ambiguous as there is doubt as to whether pure NO_2 is intended or its equilibrium mixture with N_2O_4 (see 5.3.2). On the other hand, '2 mol of NO_2' is unambiguous, NO_2 being a convenient conceptual entity (whether obtainable pure or not). *(continued)*

This emphasises that the entity specified need not be capable of isolation, or indeed of independent existence. For example:

n(Cl) = amount of Cl, amount of chlorine atoms

n(Cl$_2$) = amount of Cl$_2$, amount of chlorine molecules

n(NaCl) = amount of NaCl (whether we describe NaCl as an ion pair, or whatever)

n($\frac{1}{5}$KMnO$_4$) = amount of (entities) $\frac{1}{5}$KMnO$_4$

n(C=C) = amount of carbon-carbon double bonds (C=C)

n(2H$_2$(g) + O$_2$(g) → 2H$_2$O(g)) = amount of the reaction represented by the equation (i.e. when 2 mol H$_2$ react with 1 mol O$_2$)

molar
The word 'molar' is now restricted to the meaning 'divided by the amount of substance'. The subscript $_m$ is used unless there is no risk of ambiguity.

Thus molar volume $V_m = V/n$. Exceptions occur in the terms 'molar conductivity' and 'molar absorption coefficient'. In these two contexts 'molar' means 'divided by concentration'. Note: the word 'molar' should never to applied to 'concentration'. Strictly, 'molar concentration' is meaningless; loosely it means 'concentration of 1 mol dm^{-3}' and should not be used with 16–19 year-olds.

molar mass
The molar mass of an entity is the mass of some quantity of that entity divided by the amount of substance of that same quantity.

For example, if 0.5 mol of H$_2$O has a mass of 9.0 g, the molar mass of H$_2$O is

$$M(\text{H}_2\text{O}) = \frac{9.0\ \text{g}}{0.5\ \text{mol}} = 18\ \text{g mol}^{-1}$$

The units of molar mass are g mol^{-1} (etc.).

'Molar mass' is not 'the mass of one mole, m(H$_2$O)' (this is a mass and has units 'kg', etc.), nor is it a synonym for 'relative molecular mass, M_r(H$_2$O)' (which is a dimensionless number and has no units).

Some authors confuse 'molar mass' with 'the mass of one mole', defining either, or sometimes both, as 'the relative molecular mass expressed in grams'. A dimensionless number cannot be expressed in any units, whether grams or anything else. See Chapter 10 on quantity algebra.

molecular entity
This very useful term has been defined by IUPAC as meaning: *Any chemically or isotopically distinct atom, molecule, ion, ion-pair, radical, radical-ion, complex, conformer, etc., capable of identification as a separately distinguishable entity.* For school use the shorter term 'entity' is recommended.

A set of chemically identical (molecular) entities is termed a *chemical species*. Chemical names and formulae are commonly used to refer either to chemical species or to molecular entities, according to the context. Natural isotopic abundance is assumed unless otherwise stated (as in referring to 1.0 mol of the entity NaCl). (See also species, 9.2G.)

9.2G   Chemical reactions

acidic
See Brønsted–Lowry, see also 9.2N.

atomic structure
To a chemist, 'atomic structure' refers to the structure of the atom itself, i.e. the numbers of protons and neutrons in the nucleus of the atom and to the number and arrangement of the extra-nuclear electrons. In Earth science (see 9.2N) the meaning is synonymous with 'crystal structure' of a solid material such as a mineral.

basic
See Brønsted–Lowry, see also 9.2N.

Brønsted–Lowry
The Brønsted–Lowry theory of acids and bases involves proton transfer. 'An acid is a species (q.v. see 9.2G below) having a tendency to lose a proton.' 'A base is a species having a tendency to add on a proton.' Alternatively, 'an acid is a proton donor and a base is a proton acceptor'. When ethanoic acid and aqueous ammonia are mixed an equilibrium is set up:

$$\text{CH}_3\text{CO}_2\text{H(aq)} + \text{NH}_3\text{(aq)} \rightleftharpoons \text{CH}_3\text{CO}_2^-\text{(aq)} + \text{NH}_4^+\text{(aq)}$$

acid 1   base 2   base 1   acid 2

CH_3CO_2H and NH_4^+ are acids; $CH_3CO_2^-$ and NH_3 are bases. An acid is 'conjugate' to a base if they are related by the transfer of one proton. So here acid 1 and base 1 are conjugate, and so are acid 2 and base 2. On the other hand the acid H_3PO_4 and the base HPO_4^{2-} are not conjugate, because they differ by more than one proton (two, in fact).

A strong acid (or base) is one that is largely or completely ionised in dilute aqueous solution. For example, aqueous hydrogen chloride at a concentration of 0.1 mol dm^{-3} is almost completely ionised:

$$HCl(aq) + H_2O(l) \rightleftharpoons H^+(aq) + Cl^-(aq)$$

For a 'weak' acid such as ethanoic acid the position of equilibrium in:

$$CH_3CO_2H(aq) + H_2O(l) \rightleftharpoons CH_3CO_2^-(aq) + H_3O^+(aq)$$

lies well over to the left, even when the solution is very dilute. At a concentration of 1.0 mol dm^{-3} fewer than 1% of the ethanoic acid molecules are ionised.

The strength of an acid is affected by the solvent used: in liquid ammonia ethanoic acid (and all acids) dissociate more than they do in water. The words 'strong' and 'weak' should never be used in the context of 'concentrated' or 'dilute' – even of coffee!

'Lewis acids' and 'Lewis bases' are defined in terms of electron-pair transfer. A 'Lewis acid' is an electron-pair acceptor and a 'Lewis base' an electron-pair donor. Although a useful definition at times, the use of 'acid' and 'base' in this context can cause confusion. The Working Party recommends that the terms 'Lewis acid' and 'Lewis base' **be not used** in the 16–19 age range, although there is nothing against using 'electron-pair acceptor' and 'electron-pair donor'.

At undergraduate level acids and bases can be described as 'hard' or 'soft'. This is not recommended for the 16–19 range.

concentration

Concentration is nowadays defined as $\dfrac{\text{amount of solute}}{\text{volume of solution}}$ and its units are therefore mol dm^{-3}. The use of the word 'molarity' for this, and the letter 'M' as an abbreviation for mol dm^{-3}, are deprecated by IUPAC and they should not be used, especially in front of students.

The word 'molality' refers to $\dfrac{\text{amount of solute}}{\text{mass of solvent}}$, with units mol kg^{-1} and the possibility of confusion with 'molarity' is obvious.

If the quantity of solute is expressed as a mass then we are discussing 'mass concentration', defined as $\dfrac{\text{mass of solute}}{\text{volume of solution}}$ and having units such as g dm^{-3}. This should never be referred to as 'concentration'.

intermediate

In the context of reaction mechanisms, an 'intermediate' is a species (see 9.2G) formed during the course of a reaction which is later converted to another intermediate or the reaction products. An intermediate has a real existence, not necessarily a very long one – sometimes only a tiny fraction of a second – and is therefore contrasted with a 'transition state', an arrangement of atoms and molecules, etc., which is passed through during a reaction and not halted at.

TS$_1$ and TS$_2$ represent the enthalpies of transition states. RI represents the enthalpy of a reaction intermediate. ΔH is the enthalpy change for the reaction, and here is drawn for an exothermic reaction (Figure 9.4).

See also 9.2N.

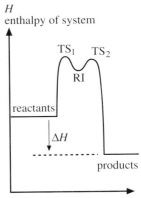

Figure 9.4
Enthalpy reaction co-ordinate diagram.

octane rating	The octane rating of petrol expresses the ability of the petrol/air mixture to resist pre-ignition (resulting in 'knocking' or 'pinking') as it is compressed in the engine during the compression stroke. The petrol is tested in a specially-designed engine and compared with artificial mixtures of 2,2,4-trimethylpentane (octane rating 100) and heptane (rating 0). The octane rating of the petrol is the percentage of 2,2,4-trimethylpentane in the artificial mixture having the same pre-ignition properties as the petrol tested. For example, ordinary unleaded petrol has an octane rating of 95 so *behaves as if* it contains 95% of 2,2,4-trimethylpentane and 5% heptane. (It need not actually *contain* a single molecule of either of these compounds.) The trivial name of 2,2,4-trimethylpentane is 'isooctane', hence the term 'octane rating'.
osmosis	'Osmosis' is the process of the passage of solvent from a less concentrated to a more concentrated solution through a 'selectively permeable membrane' (or 'semipermeable membrane'). A selectively permeable membrane allows the passage of solvent through it but not that of solute. The 'osmotic pressure' of a solution is that pressure applied to it which just prevents osmosis from pure solvent on the other side of the selectively permeable membrane (i.e. the system is in a state of dynamic equilibrium: molecules of solvent pass at equal rates in each direction through the membrane so the net flow is zero.) Osmosis is *not* filtration: a filter allows both solvent and solute molecules to pass through it. Terms such as 'solution pressure' are not used by chemists but sometimes appear in biology texts.
	In 'reverse osmosis', used in many countries for the desalination of seawater (e.g. Fuerteventura in the Canary Isles) pressure is applied to seawater separated from fresh water by a selectively permeable membrane. Water flows through the membrane from the seawater to the fresh water, thus providing a supply of desalinated water.
	See 9.2M.
plastic (noun)	A 'plastic' is a synthetic organic material which at some stage can be moulded into the desired shape. The moulding is usually carried out by the application of heat and/or pressure: sometimes, as in the case of glass-reinforced polyester, GRP, or adhesives such as Araldite, the moulding process takes place at room temperature and with brushing or wiping as the only force. *Thermoplastics* soften on heating and can be remoulded (and this cycle repeated many times). *Thermosets* do not soften on heating although they may decompose. See 9.2N.
	'Plastic' can also be used as an adjective, e.g. 'plastic raincoat'.
plasticiser	A plasticiser can be thought of as an 'intermolecular lubricant', allowing molecules of a plastic to move past each other to some extent, so that what would otherwise have been a rigid material becomes flexible. For example, poly(chloroethene), pvc, in its unplasticised form is rigid and used for making window frames and plastic drainpipes. When plasticised it is flexible enough to be used for making garments such as waterproof coats and hats.
pure	The everyday use of the word 'pure' – as in 'pure water', 'pure air', 'pure honey' etc. – means little more than 'uncontaminated' or 'wholesome'. The water will contain dissolved air and other substances; air is a mixture and so is honey.
	The scientific meaning is 'containing only one substance'. The substance may be atomic ('pure carbon'), molecular ('pure oxygen', 'pure water', 'pure ethanol') or ionic ('pure sodium chloride', 'pure chalk'). No account is taken of structure (diamond, graphite and the fullerenes may all be 'pure carbon'; red and white forms may both be 'pure phosphorus'; the cubic, tetragonal and rhombic forms may all be 'pure tin') or of state ('pure water', 'pure ice'). Nor does the isotopic composition matter, although except in rare circumstances the natural isotopic composition is expected. ('Enriched uranium', i.e. uranium containing a higher proportion than normal of $^{234}_{92}U$ is still 'pure uranium'.)
	That having been said, the concept of total purity is 'pure' fantasy! In practice *it cannot ever be achieved*. For example, if in 12.0000 g of carbon-12 only one billionth (i.e. 1 in 10^9) of the atoms are *not* carbon, that will mean that in the region of 10^{14} or 10^{15} impurity atoms are present in that 12.0000 g sample ...
	From this, it seems sensible, in any scientific context, to avoid the use of the word 'pure' unless some indication of the degree of purity is given ('99.999% pure silicon', '99+% pure sugar') or the method used to ensure a high degree of purity is stated ('water purified by deionisation', '*N*-phenylethanamide purified by three recrystallisations'.)

Common observations used to assess purity include sharpness of melting-point (for crystalline solids) and no depression of freezing temperature or elevation of boiling point (for liquids). Observers should here bear in mind the existence of eutectic mixtures and azeotropic mixtures!

solid solution
: A mixture of two or more solid components all in the same solid phase, i.e. homogeneous, for example, some metal alloys. See also 9.2N.

species
: A general term, where there is no need to be specific, for a reacting particle, usually in the context of a reaction mechanism; a 'species' can be an atom, a molecule, an ion or a radical. The formal definition of the term *chemical species* is: *A set of chemically identical atomic or molecular structural units in a solid array or of chemically identical molecular entities the members of which have the same composition and can explore the same set of molecular energy levels on the time scale of the experiment.* See section 9.2F (molecular entity). (Students in the 16–19 age range will almost certainly find this formal definition too complicated.) See also 9.2M and 9.2N.

surfactant
: A surface-active agent; one which reduces the surface tension of water. It has a double action: it helps 'wetting' of a surface and also it assists removal of dirt and grease particles. Surfactant molecules are chain-like, with one end capable of interacting with water ('hydrophilic') and the other, usually hydrocarbon, 'repelled' by water but capable of interacting with, e.g. oil ('hydrophobic'). A surfactant such as soap or washing-up liquid is capable of forming an emulsion with water and a small amount of oil and grease.

volatiles
: Applies to the lowest-boiling components of a mixture, usually in the context of petrochemicals and the refining of crude oil. See also 9.2N.

9.2H Material properties

cementation
: 1: The setting of a plastic material (particularly used in the context of dentistry).
2: Heating wrought iron in a bed of charcoal and haematite to convert it to steel (blister steel).
3: Heating one metal in contact with another to coat it.
See also 9.2N.

ductile/malleable
: Applied to metals, means much the same as 'plastic' in Earth science (see 9.2N). A ductile/malleable metal can sustain large deformations beyond its elastic limit without fracture. 'Ductile' is used when the metal is *pulled* out into wires and 'malleable' when it is *compressed,* by hammering or rolling, into thin sheets.

hardness
: See also 9.2N and 3.2N.13.

9.2I Electricity

'Electricity' is a general-purpose word used inaccurately in place of 'Electric(al) charge', 'Electric(al) current', 'Electrical energy', 'Energy transmitted/transferred electrically', 'Power transmitted/transferred electrically' ('Electrical power'?). It is used indiscriminately in place of all of the above terms, often in the same passage, thus ensuring that we do not (*because we cannot*) think clearly about the physical processes involved. 'We pay for the electricity we use.' Do we?

A kettle transfers energy electrically; power lines (sic) are used to transmit energy electrically (while, of course, some energy is unavoidably transferred within them). Old-fashioned mills had overhead shafts rotated by a water wheel or a steam engine; these transmitted energy *mechanically* to the looms and spindles. They do not transmit 'mechanicity'.

emf/pd:

emf
: emf is the measure of the energy a *source* can transfer per coulomb when that coulomb completes the circuit. The coulomb loses no energy, but the source does. (emf is an abbreviation for electromotive force, which is not, of course, a force.)

pd
: pd is a measure of the energy per coulomb transferred in a *sink* when one coulomb passes through that sink (lamp, resistor, motor, etc.).

9.2J Electric and magnetic fields

9.2K Electrochemistry

9.2K.1 Cell reactions and cell diagrams

cell diagrams

Cell reactions should be represented by a diagram (which is *not* the same as a drawing) such as:

$$Zn(s) \,|\, Zn^{2+}(aq) \,\vdots\, Cu^{2+}(aq) \,|\, Cu(s)$$

In accordance with international convention, a vertical solid line represents a phase boundary and a vertical broken line represents a liquid junction. In cases in which it has been assumed that the junction potential at a liquid junction has been eliminated (as will normally be assumed in calculations), two parallel broken lines are used:

$$Zn(s) \,|\, Zn^{2+}(aq) \,\vdots\vdots\, Cu^{2+}(aq) \,|\, Cu(s)$$

The emf E of such a cell is defined as the limiting value (for zero current) of the electrode potential for the half-cell on the *right* minus the electrode potential of the half-cell on the *left*.

When the equation for the reaction in this cell is written, it *must* be written with the Zn(s) on the left:

$$Zn(s) + Cu^{2+}(aq) \rightleftharpoons Zn^{2+}(aq) + Cu(s)$$

This convention leads to a positive value of E if the reaction actually takes place from left to right as written, when current is allowed to flow. In other words, a positive value of E indicates that the reaction is thermodynamically (thought not necessarily kinetically) feasible.

9.2K.2 Electrode potential

electrode potential

The *electrode potential* (sometimes called the reduction potential) of an electrode (half-cell) is by definition the emf of a cell in which the electrode on the *left* is a standard hydrogen electrode, and that on the *right* is the electrode in question.

For example, to measure the electrode potential of zinc the zinc electrode, written as $Zn^{2+}(aq) \,|\, Zn(s)$, is on the right and the cell is:

$$Pt \,|\, H_2(g) \,|\, H^+(aq) \,\vdots\vdots\, Zn^{2+}(aq) \,|\, Zn(s)$$

The 'half-cell reaction' taking place at the zinc electrode may be written as:

$$Zn^{2+}(aq) + 2e^- \rightleftharpoons Zn(s)$$

This is to be regarded as equivalent to the overall reaction:

$$Zn^{2+}(aq) + H_2(g) \rightleftharpoons Zn(s) + 2H^+(aq)$$

When both the hydrogen and the zinc electrodes are in standard state the emf of this cell has a value of -0.763 V.

The 'standard electrode potential' $E^{\ominus}(298\ K)$ of the zinc electrode is therefore -0.763 V.

This information can be stated unambiguously in the form:

$$Zn^{2+}(aq) \,|\, Zn(s); \quad E^{\ominus}(298\ K) = -0.763\ V$$

If the convention of having *the hydrogen electrode on the left* is not adhered to, then the measured value of the cell emf must *not* be referred to as the 'electrode potential'.

Note that such an expression for a standard electrode potential has the reduced form on the right of the half-cell, e.g. here:

$$Zn^{2+}(aq) \,|\, Zn(s)$$

And not

$$Zn(s) \,|\, Zn^{2+}(aq)$$

A consequence of the above definition is that the standard electrode potential of a standard hydrogen electrode is zero. A further consequence is that the value for E, the emf of a cell, becomes, under standard conditions:

The standard electrode potential for the half cell on the right minus the standard electrode potetial of the half cell on the left.

i.e. $\Delta E^{\ominus} = E^{\ominus}_{R} - E^{\ominus}_{L}$

So the emf for any redox cell process under standard conditions can be obtained by considering the standard electrode potentials ('SEP') of the two half-cell reactions, changing the sign of the SEP of the reaction in the left-hand cell, and then adding the two values.

9.2K.3 The Faraday constant

Faraday constant

The Faraday constant F $(= Le)$ is the ratio $\dfrac{\text{charge}}{\text{amount of substance}}$ for the proton. Its usual unit is $C\ mol^{-1}$. (Defining F in terms of the proton prevents it from having a negative value.)

The word 'Faraday', used as a unit, is the name of an obsolete unit of charge; sentences containing this concept should be rephrased either in terms of a charge expressed in coulombs or in terms of the transfer of a 'mole of electrons' or a 'mole of singly-charged ions'.

9.2L   Sound

9.2M   Biology

species

A group of similar organisms potentially able to produce fertile offspring by interbreeding amongst themselves. See also 9.2G and 9.2N.

water potential

This term is often confused with the term 'osmotic pressure' (see 9.2G). However, water potential relates to the movement of water in and out of living systems, across a selectively permeable membrane (or semipermeable membrane), due to the forces exerted by osmosis and physical pressure.

The equation for water potential is

water potential = solute potential + pressure potential

$$\phi \qquad\qquad\qquad \phi_s \qquad\qquad\qquad \phi_p$$

All these potentials are measured in pascal or kilopascal.

Solute potential is the highest osmotic pressure exerted by a solution. Pure water has the highest potential for osmotic pressure. As solutes are dissolved in pure water so the potential it can exert through osmosis will fall. The water potential for pure water is defined as zero. By definition the water potential of a solution is therefore negative. Water moves, by osmosis, to a solution which is negative from one which is closer to, or at, zero. (Solute potential was previously also called 'osmotic pressure' or 'osmotic potential'.)

Pressure potential is the mechanical pressure exerted on a solution inside a living system. For example, a plant cell contains a solution which has a quite negative solute potential. Water moves into the cell from the surrounding (weaker) solution by osmosis, but at the same time the cell swells and the cell wall exerts an increasing pressure on the expanding cell contents. As this pressure increases so water in the cell is forced out through the selectively permeable cell membrane (the solutes cannot pass through it). Eventually the pressure potential exerted by the cell wall is equal to the solute potential of the cell contents. The result is no net inflow or outflow of water. (Pressure potential was previously known as 'turgor pressure' or 'wall pressure'.) In the example above, pressure potential is positive and balances the negative solute potential. In xylem where the water column is under tension, the pressure potential is negative, helping to maintain the water flow.

9.2N   Earth science

acidic	This applies to an igneous rock with 10% or more free quartz, or containing 66% or more of silica, free or combined. The term is derived from an early view that silica was present in igneous rocks as silicic acid, which is not the case. It is now being replaced by 'silicic' or 'felsic', where 'felsic' refers to the high feldspar content of silicic rocks. See also 9.2G.
amplitude	The maximum displacement of an oscillation (wave) from the mean; half the wave height (used in Earth science in describing ocean and earthquake waves and folded rocks). See 9.2B.
assemblage	A group of fossils. See life/death assemblage (below).
association	A group of fossils commonly found together, often representing the remains of a living group of organisms.
asthenosphere/low velocity zone	A weak zone in the upper mantle below the rigid lithosphere. It is found at varying depths down to about 350 km and partly coincides with the seismic 'low velocity zone' where the velocity of P and S waves is reduced. It has plastic characteristics (see below) and so is able to flow, over geological time, allowing convection currents related to plate tectonic movement to develop.
atomic structure	The regular three-dimensional arrangement of the atoms in a unit cell. *Note*: Although the meaning of this term in chemistry is quite different, it is sufficiently well known not to need definition in 9.2G. It is nevertheless mentioned there, to highlight the difference in usage between the two branches of science.
	Perhaps 'atomic structure' should be replaced by 'crystal structure'. This would be the 'regular three-dimensional arrangement of the particles in a unit cell'. Here the particles could be atoms (as in quartz) or ions (as in many minerals) or molecules (as in ice) and a source of confusion would be abolished.
basic	This applies to igneous rocks containing much less silica than felsic rocks (see 'acidic' above), about 45–55% silica, free or combined but with no visible quartz. The term is being replaced by 'mafic', relating to the high magnesium and iron content of these rocks. See also 9.2G.
cement	1: an industrial product from the processing of limestones, e.g. Portland Cement.
	2: material precipitated into the pores of a sediment via groundwater circulation during lithification, which then holds the grains or 'clasts' together. 'Matrix' is mud that plays a similar role but suggests that the binding material is contemporary.
cementation	The crystallisation of minerals in the pore spaces of sedimentary rocks during lithification.
cleavage	1: a preferred direction of splitting in a mineral which is controlled by the atomic (see above) structure of the mineral and can therefore be diagnostic of that mineral.
	2: the tendency for fine-textured metamorphic rocks to split along flat planes in a preferred direction. Commonly associated with slate. Splitting occurs because of the parallel growth of sheet-like minerals, such as mica, orthogonal (at right angles) to the regional stresses during low-grade metamorphism.
correlation	The identification of rocks or fossils that formed at approximately the same time. They have the same relative age in the sequence of the surrounding rocks. See 'age' in 8.2N.
diagenesis	The series of processes, such as compaction and cementation, to which a sediment is subjected after burial, at temperatures and pressures less than those that cause the metamorphism. Diagenesis changes sediments into sedimentary rocks.
grade	1: referring to the grain size of clasts in a sediment.
	2: a general reference to the intensity of metamorphic processes giving rise to 'low grade' or 'high grade' metamorphic rocks.
	3: in an ore body – the percentage or proportion by mass of the valuable element or mineral in the ore.
habit	Given suitable conditions for growth, the characteristic shape of a mineral is its 'habit'. Individual crystals may have habits such as tabular (broad and flat) or prismatic (elongated in one direction) and so provide clues to the crystal systems to which they belong. Aggregates of crystals may possess habits such as reniform (kidney-shaped), e.g. massive haematite, or botryoidal (spheroidal aggregations), e.g. malachite.

hardness	The relative resistance of crystal faces to abrasion. Tested by scratching with a tool of known hardness and comparing this with Mohs' scale (see 3.2N.13). In relation to rocks, 'strength' or 'crushing resistance' is a better term than 'hard' or 'soft' rocks, as it can be measured. See also 9.2H.
hot spot	A part of a lithospheric plate affected by a local upswelling current of hot mantle material known as a plume, with subsequent eruptions. It may be separate from active plate margins and give rise to a sequence of volcanic chains, such as those seen in Hawaii.
intermediate	This describes an igneous rock whose chemistry, as expressed by oxides, is between acidic and basic. See above and 9.2G.
ionic substitution	The replacement of one ion in a mineral lattice by another ion of similar ionic size or valency – e.g. the steady change in the chemical composition of olivine minerals from the iron-rich end member, Fe_2SiO_4, at one of the sequence through $FeMgSiO_4$ to the magnesium-rich end member, Mg_2SiO_4, at the other end of the sequence. The series of minerals so formed is called a 'solid solution series'.
life/death assemblages	An assemblage is a group of fossils. In a life assemblage the fossils will be part of a related environment, preserved approximately where they lived in life, and may be in their living positions. A death assemblage is a deposit of transported individuals that may have become sorted, broken and abraded and therefore may have had no relationship to each other except the fact of transport. 'Assemblage' is used in preference to the biological term 'community', since even a life assemblage cannot record all the life forms that may have been present in that community.
lithosphere	The rigid outer shell of the Earth comprising the crust plus the uppermost layer of the mantle above the asthenosphere. Its thickness varies from 1–2 km below oceanic ridge crests to around 130 km in older oceanic areas and down to perhaps 300 km beneath ancient continents. It is broken up into the plates involved in plate tectonic movements.
maturity	This refers to the degree of physical sorting and chemical differentiation shown by a sedimentary rock and helps describe its composition and texture. It expresses the level of weathering and transport experienced by the sediment, which may have little relation to its relative age. Sediments near their source commonly contain a range of minerals and the grains tend to be angular and poorly sorted: such sediment is 'immature'. After long distances of transportation, less-stable minerals have broken down to leave mainly quartz and grains have become rounded and sorted. This is 'mature' sediment. Related terms are 'oligomict (a conglomerate based on only a few different rock types) and 'polymict' (a conglomerate that contains clasts of many different rock types).
plastic (or ductile)(adj.)	The behaviour of materials that, under directional stress, deform permanently without fracturing – they deform and stay deformed. See 9.2G and 9.2H.
solid solution	A series of minerals with a steady change in chemical composition from one end member to another, e.g. from the iron-rich form of olivine to the magnesium-rich form. In this example the ratio of iron to magnesium changes in relation to to the composition of the magma from which the olivine is crystallising. Most major rock-forming minerals exist as solid solutions. See also 9.2G.
species/morphospecies	The biological definition of species is based on their reproductive activity, which is obviously not available to most geological specimens unless they have living representatives. Therefore in Earth science both species and genera are assigned by their physical characteristics, or morphology, that can be observed to place fossils in common groups. See also 9.2G and 9.2M.
stability fields	These mark the physical parameters, such as temperature or pressure, within which certain polymorphs will form and maintain their atomic (see above) characteristics. They may also be used to mark the parameters within which a discontinuous series of minerals may form. On a larger scale, the term is used to define the boundaries within certain metamorphic states and between metamorphism and other physical states such as melt.
suture	Essentially means a 'line' or junction. Can be used to describe some distinctive lines on fossil specimens, such as trilobite headshields or ammonite chambers. It is also used to suggest the linear geographic area formed after closure of a subduction zone.
terrestrial	This implies living in a subaerial environment, or processes pertaining to that environment, i.e. on land.

texture	The size, shape and packing of grains, minerals and other particles making up a rock. Roughness/smoothness is a separate property. The texture or 'fabric' may be used to work out how the rock formed.
Uniformitarianism	The principle that processes which operate today operated in similar ways in the past, since they were affected by the same physical, chemical and biological factors. The evolution of the Earth and its atmosphere, and of life on Earth, mean that the principle cannot always be strictly applied.
volatiles	Elements or compounds which are liquids or gases and are lost from cooling magma or, during diagenesis (see above), from sedimentary rocks (e.g. in the formation of coal). See also 9.2G.
zone fossil	An organism known to live within a limited range of geological time. To be effective, zone fossils need to be widespread to act as a marker for relative dating.

10 THE USE OF ALGEBRA

10.1 Quantity and number algebra

Scientific equations are statements written in the form of complete sentences. It is usual to write these sentences in a universal shorthand. There are two ways this can be done correctly:

(a) Using *Quantity algebra*. In this, each shorthand symbol represents both the number of the quantity and the quantity itself (e.g. the mass of an item is represented by '*m*'). On balance, the Working Party feels that the use of Quantity algbebra causes fewer mistakes and teaches the *science* better. We have used Quantity algebra throughout this book.

(b) Using *Number algebra*. In this, each item in the equation is represented by the units in which it is measured and by a symbol representing the number of those units (e.g. the mass of an item is represented by 'm kg' or 'x kg', where 'm' or 'x' is a pure number). Number algebra is rarely used at this level but an example is given in the box.

Problem: Calculate the resultant force needed to accelerate a mass of 1200 kg by 3 m s^{-2}.

(a) *Quantity algebra*

Let mass $= m$
 acceleration $= a$
 force $= F$

$F = ma$ The scientific statement, shorthand for 'force = mass × acceleration'

Substituting $m = 1200$ kg, $a = 3$ m s^{-2} in the formula,

$F = 1200$ kg $\times 3$ m s^{-2}

$= 3600$ N

So the force needed is 3600 N.

(b) *Number algebra*

EITHER

Let mass $=$ m kg
 acceleration $=$ a m s^{-2}
 force $=$ F N

Take care! Here we are using m to stand for mass *and* for metres.

F N $=$ m kg $\times$ a m s^{-2} The scientific statement, (a reminder of the physics and the Number algebra)

F $=$ m $\times$ a shorthand for 'force = mass × acceleration'

$= 1200 \times 3 = 3600$

So the force needed is 3600 N.

OR

Let mass, *m* $=$ x kg
 acceleration, *a* $=$ y m s^{-2}
 force, *F* $=$ z N

$F = m \times a$ The scientific statement, shorthand for 'force = mass × acceleration'

z N $=$ x kg $\times$ y m s^{-2}

So z $=$ x $\times$ y $= 1200 \times 3 = 3600$

So the force needed is 3600 N.

Note: When a physical law is represented by an equation of the form '$F = ma$', each symbol in that equation represents both a property of nature (e.g. 'mass') and the magnitude of that property. So when an equation is written in this form, it is written in the language of Quantity algebra. If calculations are then to be done in Number algebra, magnitudes should be represented by **other** letters (as in the second alternative in the box) in order to avoid confusion. It is easy to forget whether a hand-written 'F' represents a force or a number. Even typed *italics* are not sufficiently distinguishing.

10.2 Good and bad practice

Two simple illustrations of good and bad practice using quantity algebra are given here.

Problem 1: What resultant force is needed to give a mass of 50 kg an acceleration of 4 m s^{-2}?

Correct

Clear	**Not clear**

Let force $= F$
mass $= m$
acceleration $= a$

$F = ma$ (the scientific statement)

$F = 50 \text{ kg} \times 4 \text{ m s}^{-2}$ ——— Initial substitution of the original
$= 200$ N   units (as on left) facilitates
                                   comprehension and checking, and
                                   it reinforces the physics.

So the force needed is 200 N.

Let force $= F$
mass $= m$
acceleration $= a$

$F = ma$ (the scientific statement)

$F = 50 \times 4$ N $= 200$ N ——— Substitution without
                                     units does not allow
                                     units to be checked.

So the force needed is 200 N.

Incorrect

Let force $= F$
mass $= m$
acceleration $= a$

$F = ma$ (the scientific statement)

$F = 50 \times 4 = 200$ ——— Omission of units when
                               substituting leads to an
                               incorrect statement. The
                               force F is not 200.

So the force needed is 200 N.

Note: To be *correct*, an argument must consist of complete sentences, and these sentences must be logically connected. To be *clear*, all important steps must be shown (to help in the checking, as well as in the comprehension).

Problem 2: At what temperature will 16.0 g of oxygen gas occupy a volume of 8.00 dm^3 at a pressure of 130 000 Pa? (The value of the gas constant is 8.31 J K^{-1} mol^{-1}.)

Let pressure $= p$, volume $= V$, temperature $= T$, amount of oxygen gas in moles $= n$.

Using $pV = nRT$, where $R =$ gas constant $= 8.31$ J K^{-1} mol^{-1} (the scientific statement), and rearranging,

$$T = \frac{pV}{nR}$$

The amount n of oxygen gas can be calculated from

$$n = \frac{16.0 \text{ g}}{32.0 \text{ g mol}^{-1}} = 0.500 \text{ mol}$$

Substituting,

$$T = \frac{130\ 000 \text{ Pa} \times 8.00 \times 10^{-3} \text{ m}^3}{0.500 \text{ mol} \times 8.31 \text{ J K}^{-1} \text{ mol}^{-1}}$$
$$= \frac{130 \times 8.00}{0.500 \times 8.31} \text{ K}$$
$$= 250 \text{ K}$$

Checking the units:

$$\frac{\text{Pa m}^3}{\text{mol J K}^{-1} \text{ mol}^{-1}}$$
$$= \frac{\text{N m}^{-2} \text{ m}^3}{\text{N m K}^{-1}}$$
$$= \text{K}$$

So the temperature is 250 K.

11 MATHEMATICAL TOPICS

11.1 Mathematical conventions

In recent years, in the interests of eventual international harmonisation, various changes have been made in the International and British Standards governing the preparation of printed scientific material. It is recommended that, where practicable, handwritten scientific material should also be prepared in accordance with the Standards. The following conventions are of particular relevance:

Numbers: The decimal marker should be a dot on the line (*not* a dot half-high). Before and after the decimal point, digits may be grouped in threes to make for ease of reading but it is usual to write 1000, not 1 000. Commas should *not* be used to separate groups of three digits. With a number less than unity, a zero should be placed before the decimal point.

Multiplication sign: The multiplication sign between numbers *should* be a cross, and this *may* also be used to indicate multiplication of physicochemical quantities. A dot on the line should not be used to indicate multiplication in any circumstances because of confusion with the decimal marker. Multiplication of symbols for units should normally be indicated by leaving a space between the symbols.

Letter symbols: Letter symbols, for numbers other than mathematical constants, should be in italics.

Quantity algebra is used throughout (see Chapter 10).

11.1.1 Mathematical symbols

$\times$	multiplied by
$=$	is equal to
	is not equal to
$\equiv$	is approximately equal to
$\propto$	is proportional to
$<$	is less than
	is less than or equal to
$>$	is greater than
	is greater than or equal to
$\ll$	is much less than
$\gg$	is much greater than
∞	infinity
Σ	the sum of
Π	the product of
$\bar{a}$	the mean value of a
$\ln a$	the natural logarithm of a
$\lg a$	the common logarithm (base 10) of a
$\log_x a$	the logarithm to base x of a
$\exp a$ or e^a	the exponential of a

$\in$	is a member of, is an element of, or belongs to
$\notin$	is not a member of
$\subset$	is a sub-set of
$\cup$	the union of two sets
$\cap$	the intersection of two sets
$\varnothing$	the empty (or null) set
ε or ν	the universal set
$\Rightarrow$	implies that
$\Leftrightarrow$	if, and only if
	or implies, and is implied by
	or is logically equivalent to
( )	parentheses
[ ]	brackets
{ }	braces

Braces are used to enclose the elements of a set or the description of the elements of a set.

11.1.2 Use of the solidus

When unit symbols are combined as a quotient, e.g. metre per second, it is recommended that they be written as m s^{-1}. The use of a solidus is permitted, e.g. m/s, **but should only be necessary at an elementary level**. In no case should the solidus be used twice in a derived unit as this leads to ambiguity of interpretation.

Thus the SI unit for acceleration **must not** be written m/s/s; it is written as m s^{-2}, or if necessary, m/s^2. Similarly the unit of specific heat capacity is J kg^{-1} K^{-1}, although J/(kg K) is permitted. For the use of the solidus to indicate the division of a physical quantity by a unit, see Section 11.2.

11.1.3 Roman numerals

The Roman system is cumbersome and has no zero, no fractions and no negative numbers. Certain numbers are represented by (capital) letters:

I	= 1
V	= 5
X	= 10
L	= 50
C	= 100
D	= 500
M	= 1000

All other numbers are expressed as a combination of these. Each letter is repeated as many times as necessary, in descending order of magnitude. For example, 25 is XXV and 1733 is MDCCXXXIII. If (one only) letter representing a smaller number is written before the larger, it is subtracted.

So IX = 9, XC = 90, MCM = 1900. V and L are not used in this way.

The year 2000 is written as MM, and 2001 as MMI.

11.2 Tables and graphs

Tables of values of physical quantities should be headed by the physical quantities divided by the units (see Example on right). The entries in the tables are then (pure) numbers and express the ratios of the physical quantities to the unit quantities.

The use of the solidus to indicate the division of a physical quantity by its unit has advantages, **provided that care is taken not to use a solidus in the unit itself**. It enables the unit to retain its familiar form and, at elementary level, may be verbalised as 'in' thus allowing correct notation to be used at that level.

The operation of taking a logarithm can be performed only upon a number. In some instances, e.g. $\lg(t/s)$, it is immediately apparent that a number is involved. In cases such as the (incorrect) definition of pH as '$-\log_{10}[H^+]_{aq}$' the physical quantity $[H^+]_{aq}$ must in fact be converted to a pure number 'by dividing by the units' or formally by dividing by $[H^+]_{aq}^{\ominus}$ which is 1 mol dm^{-3} by definition. (See Section 11.8.1 for a discussion of pH and logarithms.)

The axes of a graph are marked off in numbers. Care should be taken to avoid appearing to plot a graph of anything other than a (pure) number. The correct labelling of axes leads to correct units for gradients. It may be useful to choose scales so that a straight line slopes at an angle of 30° to 60°, so making maximum use of the graph paper. There are advantages in using multiples of 2, 5 or 10 divisions to ease the plotting of points between the rulings. The convention is that the y (or vertical) axis is used for the dependent variable, which is being plotted against the independent variable on the x (or horizontal) axis.

Whether the line on a graph is straight or not, it is always referred to as a 'curve'.

Points on a graph should not be plotted as dots, although a dot with a circle round it, ⊙, is suitable. Many people favour a vertical cross, +, because the vertical and the horizontal lines can be plotted separately, leading to a precise position for the point. The length of the vertical line can be used to indicate the uncertainty of the measured value.

┼ indicates a more uncertain value (on the y axis) than +. All the horizontal lines on the graph should be equal since there is little uncertainty about the value of the independent variable.

The saltire, ×, is not so easy to plot precisely and the Working Party suggests that it be not used.

Example

The data used come from an experiment to find out how the effective force F propelling a boat at constant velocity v is related to the velocity.

If $F = 200$ N, then $F/N = 200$.

'$F/N = 200$' means 'The number of (newton) units of which the force consists = 200.'

Table headings and graph axes are labelled as below:

$v/\text{m s}^{-1}$	F/N
2.0	25
3.0	53
4.0	96
5.0	150
6.0	217

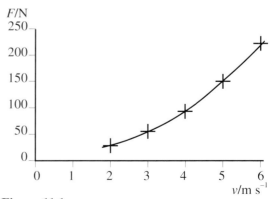

Figure 11.1
Graph of force against velocity.

In this example, it is suspected that there is a power relationship between F and v.

Assuming that $F = kv^n$ and n is dimensionless,

$$k = \frac{F}{v^n}$$

Taking logarithms, here to base 10:

$$\log \frac{F}{N} = \log \frac{k}{k \text{ units}} + n \log \frac{v}{\text{m s}^{-1}}$$

$\log_{10}(v/\text{m s}^{-1})$	$\log_{10}(F/N)$
0.30	1.39
0.48	1.724
0.60	1.981
0.70	2.175
0.78	2.336

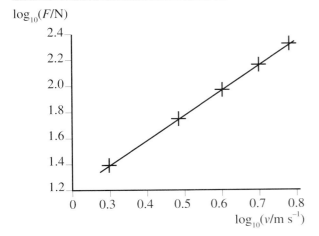

Figure 11.2
Graph of $\log_{10}(F/N)$ against $\log_{10}(v/\text{m s}^{-1})$.

It is also possible to use 'log-log' paper (Figure 11.3): the data are plotted as in the first table and the scale on the paper converts the figures to logarithms. However it is then less easy to calculate k and n.

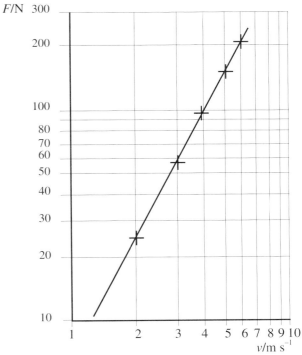

Figure 11.3
Graph of force against velocity plotted on log-log paper.

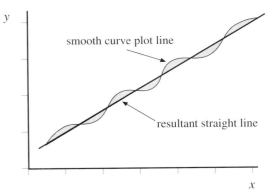

Figure 11.4
Finding the line of best fit when a straight line is expected.

Lines of best fit

The readings plotted in the example above are somewhat artificial, in that the five points lie exactly on a smooth curve or straight line. In real life, uncertainties in the readings may suggest that the points lie close to a smooth curve or a straight line, but a line drawn through each point can only be described as 'wiggly'. Using the rule 'equal areas either side', the *line of best fit* can be found.

If the line of best fit seems to be a straight line, use a transparent ruler. Adjust the position of the ruler until the areas between the ruler and the curve above and the ruler and the curve below seem to be about equal (see Figure 11.4). The line of best fit can then be drawn.

Similarly for a line of best fit that is curved, various possible lines can be pencilled in until the areas above and below a particular line are adjudged equal.

In the example it is assumed that all the intermediate readings, not just the five actually plotted, would fall on the curve plotted. It is therefore reasonable to drawn a smooth curve between the points plotted.

This is not always the case. For example, a series of readings of noon temperatures on the roof of some building would (particularly in our British climate!) give an erratic set of points subject to no general mathematical relationship such as $F = kv^n$. The points could then be joined by a series of *straight* lines or expressed as a spike chart (see Section 11.4).

11.3 Pie charts

These should be drawn adjacent to their tables of data and have informative titles. The sectors should be put in rank order starting at 'noon' and proceeding clockwise. They should be restricted to broad categories, preferably no more than six, and there should be no sub-division of the sectors unless vital.

Table and pie chart showing world primary energy consumption in 1982 (millions of tonnes oil equivalent)

Energy source	Energy consumption 1982
oil	2819
coal	2041
natural gas	1312
water power	446
nuclear energy	217
total	6835

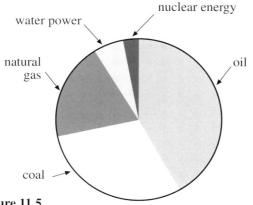

Figure 11.5
A pie chart.

Short titles may be written in their sectors, longer titles must be outside the circle for clarity.

If two pie charts are compared (e.g. consumption for 1962 and 1982) the sequence of segments should be the same for both, regardless of relative sizes.

11.4 Bar charts, column graphs and histograms

These categories of display are superficially similar in that they are used for the display of discrete values. A clear distinction, however, should be made between data for which the sum of the values would have *no* meaning, and data for which the sum of the values *does* have meaning, and the form of the display should reflect this distinction, as the following examples show. If 'thin bars' (narrow rectangles of equal width) are to be used **they should not touch when the sum of the values has no meaning**.

Table and spike chart showing the variation of first ionisation energy (I) of elements with atomic number (Z)

Element	Z	I/kJ mol^{-1}
hydrogen	1	1310
helium	2	2370
lithium	3	519
beryllium	4	900
boron	5	799
carbon	6	1090
nitrogen	7	1400
oxygen	8	1310
fluorine	9	1680
neon	10	2080

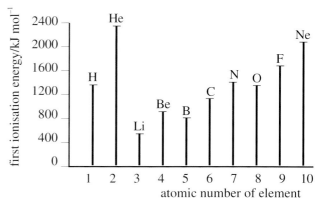

Figure 11.6
A spike chart.

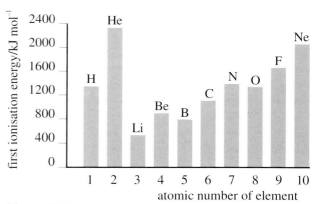

Figure 11.7
A 'thin-bar' chart, an alternative to the spike chart.

Column graphs are drawn when plotting frequency distributions with discrete data (e.g. frequency of occurrence of nests with different numbers of eggs, see Figure 11.8). The blocks should be drawn in order of increasing or decreasing magnitude and they should not touch. Each block should be labelled centrally.

Table and column graph showing the frequency of nests containing different numbers of eggs

Number of eggs per nest	Numbers of nests
1	0
2	0
3	1
4	3
5	15
6	14
7	4
8	2
9	1
10	0

Table and histogram showing frequency of occurrence of leaves of different lengths

Leaf length/mm	Numbers
100–110	1
110–120	7
120–130	8
130–140	14
140–150	18
150–160	16
160–170	9
170–180	10
180–190	5
190–200	1

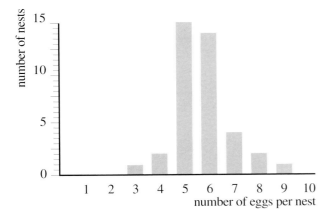

Figure 11.8
A column graph.

The sum of the values does have a meaning here – it is the total number of eggs in the 40 nests being considered. Some people would therefore call this column graph a histogram (see below) and draw the blocks as touching.

Histograms are drawn when plotting frequency distributions with continuous data (e.g. frequency of occurrence of leaves of different lengths, see Figure 11.9). The blocks should be drawn in order of decreasing or increasing magnitude and they should be touching. The edges of the blocks should be labelled. Thus a block might be labelled '7' at the left and '8' at the right. This is expressed as a class range 7–8 units, but it is implied that 7.0 is included in this range but 8.0 is not reached. 8.0 will belong in the next class, range 8–9.

When displaying frequency density (frequency per unit class width) by means of a histogram, care must be taken over boundary values. Thus, for the percentages of copper found in samples of copper(II) oxide the selected ranges might be 76–77 (to include 76.0 but not 77.0), 77–78 (to include 77.0 but not 78.0), 78–79…

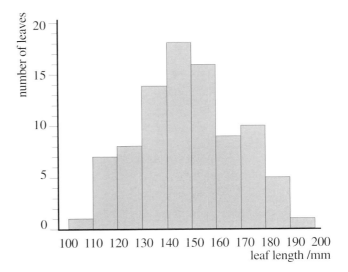

Figure 11.9
A histogram.

If discrete quantities are to be studied they should be treated as extending half a unit either side. Thus, for classifying molecules by their vibrational energies the classes would be $-\frac{1}{2}$ to $\frac{1}{2}$, $\frac{1}{2}$ to $\frac{3}{2}$, $\frac{3}{2}$ to $\frac{5}{2}$, … Although each class appears to include 'impossible' values no confusion arises because all real values may be assigned unambiguously.

As the class width decreases a histogram may approximate to a continuous distribution such as:
(a) a normal distribution curve (as in the case of the proportions of copper in samples of copper(II) oxide)
(b) an exponential distribution curve (as in the case of the activity of a radionuclide in isolation)
(c) a Boltzmann distribution curve (as in the case of the vibrational energies of molecules).

In each case, however, the apparently smooth curve should be regarded as a histogram.

11.5 Triangular diagrams

Triangular diagrams are valuable for illustrating variation between three components and are used particularly in certain areas of Earth science and chemistry.

An Earth science example is the triangular plot of soil texture in terms of the three components, clay, sand and silt, as shown in Figure 11.10.

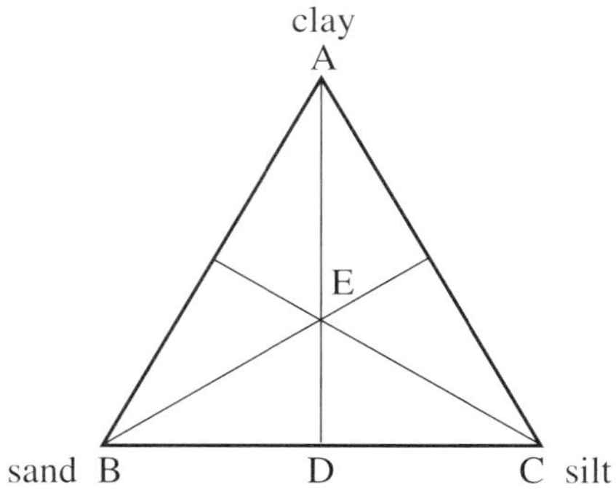

Figure 11.10
A triangular diagram used to plot soil texture.

Figure 11.11
Textural classification of soil, based on a triangular diagram.

1 clay
2 sandy clay
3 sandy clay loam
4 sandy loam
5 loamy sand
6 sand
7 clay loam
8 loam
9 silty clay
10 silty clay loam
11 silt loam
12 silt

In Figure 11.10, a plot at point A represents a pure clay soil, at point B a pure sand soil and at point C a pure silt soil. All points on the line AD represent mixtures containing equal proportions of sand and silt with different amounts of clay. At point D a soil is 50% sand, 50% silt and no clay. At any point on the line BC the soil consists of varying proportions of sand and silt, with clay absent. At point E, all three components are present in equal proportions (i.e. 33% clay, 33% sand and 33% silt).

This triangular diagram system allows soils to be classified by texture, as shown in Figure 11.11. The classification shows that the 'loam', referred to in many books on gardening, is a roughly equal mixture of sand, silt and clay.

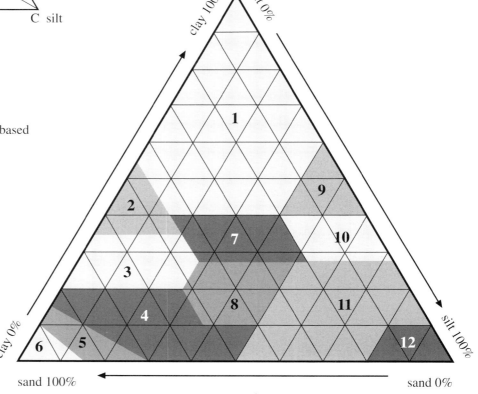

In chemistry, phase diagrams are used to show the relationship between two components and perhaps temperature. We can use triangular diagrams to show the relationship between three components at a fixed temperature. At some other temperature the diagram would be lifted above, or dropped below, the plane of the paper and the various lines would shift.

If the components are A, B and C, and at the given temperature A and B are completely miscible and A and C are completely miscible, but B and C are only partially miscible, then the triangular diagram will resemble Figure 11.12.

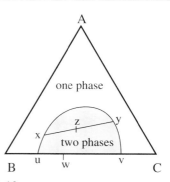

Figure 11.12
A triangular diagram indicating the miscibility of three chemical components at a certain temperature.

Examples of such systems include:
Ethanoic acid/trichloromethane/water
Ethanol/benzene/water
Ethanol/ethyl ethanoate/water

The miscibility diagram illustrates the situation at some constant value of temperature. The 'one-phase' area is that in which A, B and C are completely miscible. The area marked 'two phases' represents the various proportions of A, B and C which are only partially miscible.

Along the line BC, there is no A in the mixture. Point u represents the composition of a saturated solution of C in B, whereas point v represents the composition of a saturated solution of B in C. Figure 11.12 shows that, for these three components at this constant temperature, point w does not represent a solution of uniform composition. A solution plotted at point w represents the *overall* composition of a mixture of B and C which is actually composed of a saturated solution of C in B (of composition denoted by u) and a saturated solution of B in C (of composition v). If point w is close to point u then 'C in B' predominates and there is little 'B in C' present. If point w is near to point v the converse is true. If point w is near the centre, then the quantities of the two phases are close to being equal. The line BC is called a 'tie-line'.

If some A is added to the 'B and C mixture' then the compositions of the phases change. The point x represents the composition of a saturated solution of C in a mixture of B and A, point y a saturated solution of B in a mixture of C and A. The tie-line in this case is xy and a mixture of *overall* composition represented by point z will be a two-phase mixture, one phase of composition represented by the point x and the other, that of point y.

11.6 Accuracy and 'significant figures'

What is the difference between 'I went for a 4-mile walk' and 'I went for a 3.9-mile walk'? The first means 'I walked about 4 miles – between $3\frac{1}{2}$ and $4\frac{1}{2}$'. The second means 'The walk was fairly accurately about 3.9 miles – nearer 3.9 than 3.8 or 4.0'. The number of figures in a quantity tells us how accurately the quantity has been measured. These are called the *significant figures*.

Zeros *between* other numbers count as significant; zeros before or after the other numbers do not.

361	has 3 significant figures
3.61	has 3 significant figures
361 000	has 3 significant figures
0.003 61	has 3 significant figures
3.061	has 4 significant figures

The one exception to this rule is that zeros after a decimal point are significant:

361.00 has 5 significant figures. By quoting a value in this way we are claiming that it is smaller than 361.005 and larger than 360.995. This claims much greater precision than the use of 361, which is smaller than 361.5 and larger than 360.5.

Avoid talking in terms of *decimal places*, which in this context can be meaningless.

For example:

(a) 361, 36.1 and 0.361 are expressed to 3 significant figures but to different numbers of decimal places;

(b) 3.61, 36.13 and 361.32 are all expressed to 2 decimal places but to different numbers of significant figures;

(c) A length of 3.61 metres is the same as, and measured to exactly the same precision as, a length of 361 cm. It is significant figures that matter, not decimal places.

We have to remember to use the number of significant figures appropriate to the accuracy of the measuring or counting equipment.

Rounding off

We 'round off' a number containing more significant figures than needed by rounding *up* if the last figure is 5–9 and *down* if it is 0–4.

For example:

360.99 (5 s.f.)	*rounds*	*up to*	361.0 (4 s.f.)
	or	*up to*	361 (3 s.f.)
	or	*down to*	360 (2 s.f.)
	or	*up to*	400 (1 s.f.)

(To round from 5 s.f. to 3 s.f., you do *not* round first to 4 s.f. For example, 360.49 (5 s.f.) rounds up to 360.5 (4 s.f.) rounds up to 361 (3 s.f), but 360.49 (5 s.f.) rounds *down* to 360 (3 s.f.). To round to 3 s.f. you *only* look at the fourth figure.)

Which of these five numbers should be used depends on the accuracy of the measurements. For the 16–19 age range it will hardly ever make sense to quote more than three, and for experimental results two significant figures is probably the most realistic number.

See also the discussion of accuracy, Section 11.7.

11.7 Uncertainty and accuracy in experimental work

This example is from the evaluation of a chemistry experiment.

Example

Some comment is required on the reliability of the experiment. Any comment will depend on the particular experiment and on the results.

The word *error* is often used as a general term, but strictly speaking the error is the difference between the result obtained and the correct result. If the correct result can be looked up (in a data book, say), useful comments on error can be made. This should be done if at all possible. Without the correct value, comment on error is not possible.

However, in any experiment one can comment on *uncertainty*. If the experiment is quantitative, a quantitative estimate of the uncertainty must be made.

Quantitative uncertainty

This is uncertainty which arises from:
(a)   the accuracy of the apparatus itself
(b)   taking readings from scientific apparatus.

In *volumetric analysis* there are four pieces of scientific apparatus used for measurement. Each can be considered separately before combining the individual uncertainties to find the overall uncertainty.

Balance: The manufacturers say that the balance has a reproducibility of 0.01 g. This means that any reading has an overall uncertainty of plus or minus 0.01 g.

The uncertainty in reading the balance is 0.005 g at every reading. This means that there is this uncertainty on the first and the last reading – even if one starts at 0.00 g. The overall uncertainty is therefore $2 \times 0.005 = 0.01$ g.

A typical mass in these experiments might be 5.00 g.

The percentage uncertainty of the apparatus is therefore

$$\frac{0.01}{5.00} \times 100\% = 0.2\%$$

The percentage uncertainty in this reading is

$$\frac{0.01}{5.00} \times 100\% = 0.2\%$$

The total uncertainty in the balance is therefore $0.2 + 0.2 = 0.4\%$.

Similar uncertainties can be calculated for the burette (0.8%), the pipette (0.64%) and the volumetric flask (0.08%).

Overall uncertainty

The overall percentage uncertainty is the sum of the individual percentage uncertainties in this case (because the quantities are multiplied or divided), i.e.

$$0.4 + 0.8 + 0.64 + 0.08 = 1.92\%$$

This should be quoted as 2%. The 0.08% is not significant.

There is no advantage in this example in using a balance which measures to more than two decimal places.

If the overall answer is a concentration, say 0.105 mol dm^{-3}, the answer should be quoted as

$$0.105 \pm 0.002 \text{ mol dm}^{-3}$$

There is no point in quoting the answer to more than three significant figures, because of the uncertainty.

Experimental uncertainty

These are uncertainties which cannot be quantified and often arise from having to make a judgement.

In volumetric analysis, one has to judge when the indicator has changed colour. It is not enough simply to identify these uncertainties; the writer must say how they were minimised. For example, one can minimise the uncertainty in judging the end point by titrating until the *first* permanent orange colour is observed.

In other experiments, the uncertainty may not be one of judgement. For example, in enthalpy change experiments, there is bound to be some heat lost to the surroundings. In this case it should be clearly stated how this loss was minimised in the experiment. The writer could also go on to say how the experiment could be improved to reduce this uncertainty even further.

11.8 Logarithms

The alternative to multiplying, say, $10\,000 \times 100$ ($= 1\,000\,000$), or dividing $1000 \div 10$ ($= 100$), is to express the numbers as powers of ten and multiply them by adding the indices (or to divide, subtract). So

$$10\,000 \times 100 = 10^4 \times 10^2 = 10^{(4+2)} = 10^6 = 1\,000\,000$$

and $1000 \div 10 = 10^3 \div 10^1 = 10^{(3-1)} = 10^2 = 100$.

These indices are called the *logarithms to base 10* of the original numbers.

Any number can be expressed in this form.

Since $2 = 10^{0.301}$, therefore $\log_{10} 2 = 0.301$ (usually written as lg 2, see 11.1.1).

Before the advent of calculators, students used sets of 'logarithm tables' to convert numbers into their logarithmic equivalents, then add, subtract, etc., and finally reconvert to the answer.

Example

Multiply 2×3.

$$\log_{10} 2 = 0.301$$
$$\log_{10} 3 = 0.477$$
$$\log_{10}(2 \times 3) = 0.301 + 0.477 = 0.788$$
'antilog' (or 'inv log') $0.778 = 6$.

Logarithms are still useful for calculating cube roots if the calculator doesn't have a cube-root key. So

$$\sqrt[3]{x} = x^{\frac{1}{3}}$$

$$\sqrt[3]{8} = 8^{\frac{1}{3}} = 10^{(\log_{10} 8) \times \frac{1}{3}} = 10^{0.903 \times \frac{1}{3}} = 10^{0.301} = 2$$

Using a calculator

Key in number
Press LOG
Divide result by 3
Press INV then LOG
Read off answer

Round the answer to the appropriate number of significant figures (many students omit this stage and end up with an unrealistic result).

Natural logarithms

Calculators also have a key 'LN' or ('ln') which calculates logarithms to base e. These are known as *natural logarithms*. e, and natural logarithms, appear in many mathematical operations such as differentiation and integration.

Example

$$\int \frac{dx}{x} = \ln x + \text{constant}$$

This is a useful result in studies of the rates of radioactive disintegration and first-order chemical reactions.

Using logarithms for compression

Since logarithms involve powers of ten, a logarithmic scale compresses a set of readings into a manageable range (see Figure 11.3 and sub-section 11.8.1).

11.8.1 The pH scale

In the context of acidic and alkaline aqueous solutions, 'bench dilute' hydrochloric acid at a concentration of 2 mol dm^{-3} has a hydrogen ion concentration of about 2 mol dm^{-3}.

$[H^+]_{aq} = 2 = 10^{0.30}$ mol dm^{-3} (taking $\log_{10} 2$ to be 0.30)

In pure water at about 298 K, $[H^+]_{aq} = 10^{-7}$ mol dm^{-3}

In 'bench dilute' sodium hydroxide solution ($[NaOH] = 2$ mol dm^{-3}), $[H^+]_{aq} = 10^{-14.30}$ mol dm^{-3}

This is nearly '15 orders of magnitude' smaller than the figure for the acid. The concentration of hydrogen ions in the acid differs from that in the alkali by a factor of $10^{-14.6}$ or rather over 100 000 000 000 000 times. It would be impossible, then, to plot a graph of $[H^+]_{aq}$ against volume of titrant in the titration of an acid with an alkali. However, if we take the *logarithm to base 10* of each value of $[H^+]_{aq}$ and use these values for the y axis, we obtain a titration curve.

These logarithmic values are the basis of the *pH scale*.

$$pH = -\log_{10} \frac{[H^+]_{aq}}{[H^+]_{aq}^{\ominus}}$$

(This is the definition for the 16–19 age range, see Section 11.2. At higher levels the definition of pH is an operational one, in terms of the emf of a cell.)

So for $[H^+]_{aq} = 1$ mol dm^{-3}, pH $= 0$.

For solutions more acidic than that, and there aren't too many – e.g. $[HCl]_{aq} = 2$ mol dm^{-3}, the pH is –0.30. For most dilute and/or weak acids, pH lies between 0 and 7. Solutions which are neutral (i.e. $[H^+]_{aq} = [OH^-]_{aq}$) at about 298 K have pH $= 7$.

Note: At higher temperatures water dissociates more, though still neutral: $[H^+]_{aq} = [OH^-]_{aq} > 10^{-7}$ mol dm^{-3}, so the pH is less than 7.

For solutions on the alkaline side of neutral, up to, for example, $[NaOH] = 1$ mol dm^{-3}, the pH lies between 7 and 14. For more strongly alkaline solutions – again, as for acids, there aren't many – the pH is greater than 14.

The concept of pH can be applied to other ions, defined similarly:

$$pOH = -\log_{10} \frac{[OH^+]_{aq}}{[OH^+]_{aq}^{\ominus}}$$

The concept also applies to other solvents. For example, in liquid ammonia at its boiling point when

$$[NH_4^+]_{NH_3} = [NH_2^-]_{NH_3}$$

the pH of neutrality is about 11.

The acidity constants (K_a) of weak acids and the basicity constants (K_b) of weak bases can be similarly converted to pK_a and pK_b values. This allows the strengths of acids and bases to be tabulated in a simple way.

11.9 Some terms used in statistics

The values for the percentage of copper in copper(II) oxide found by 79 groups of pupils were as follows. Figure 11.13 is plotted using these data.

Spread of results	Number of groups with results inside spread
73.0–74	0
74.0–75	1
75.0–76	3
76.0–77	7
77.0–78	9
78.0–79	11
79.0–80	12
80.0–81	11
81.0–82	10
82.0–83	8
83.0–84	5
84.0–85	2
Over 85.0	0

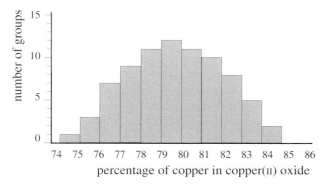

Figure 11.13
A frequency curve.

A 'typical value'

We often use the word *average* to label a typically middle-ish value out of a set of data. The word is used loosely to cover any of the three measures of 'middleness' below (it best describes the mean). It is better not to use average at all when discussing data or experimental results – and make correct use of one of the three terms explained below.

■ The **mode** is the value which appears most often – the interval is 79.0–80, so we quote the mid-point 79.5.

■ The **median**. If all the readings are put in order of size the median is the middle one. Here we have 79 sets of results so the middle one is the 40th. Again, it is in the interval 79.0–80, mid-point 79.5. **Quartiles** divide the list into quarters. Here the **first quartile** is 77.5 and the **third quartile** 81.5. The **second quartile** is the median. If the number of readings is large the terms **quintile** (= one fifth), **decile** (= one-tenth) or **percentile** (= one-hundredth) may be used.

■ The **mean**. The mean ($\bar{x}$) is calculated by adding together all the values (x) and dividing by the total number of them (N):

$$\bar{x} = \frac{\sum x}{N}$$

($\bar{x}$ is named 'x-bar'.)

The mean is given the symbol M in some books.

Root mean square

There are times when it is appropriate to calculate the **root mean square** value, for example in the context of the speeds/velocities of gas molecules:

$$\bar{x}_{\text{rms}} = \sqrt{\frac{\sum x^2}{N}}$$

because this is related to the average kinetic energies of the molecule (kinetic energy depends on v^2), and in this context it is usually energy which is being discussed. .

Range and standard deviation

To express how 'spread out' the readings are, we can quote the **range**. The range is the difference between the highest and lowest reading. In the copper example above the range is $84.5 - 74.5 = 10.0$. It is simple but crude, because one or both of these extreme values might not be reliable. The interquartile range (the difference between the first and third quartiles) is another useful measure.

A useful statistical measure of 'spread out-ness' is the **standard deviation**, σ. It is calculated and defined as:

$$\sigma = \sqrt{\frac{\sum(x - \bar{x})^2}{N}}$$

or else as

$$\sigma = \sqrt{\frac{\sum x^2}{N} - \bar{x}^2}$$

With a large number of observations we may obtain a curve called a *normal* (or *Gaussian*) distribution. (Other distributions, e.g. Poisson, may be important in other contexts.) This is a frequency curve which is 'symmetrical' (i.e. mode = median = mean) and bell-shaped. For this curve the majority of values lie reasonably close to the mean: 68% are within one standard deviation of it and 95% lie within two standard deviations of it.

The results of national tests of IQ (intelligence quotient) are often adjusted (forced) to a national mean of 100 and a standard deviation of 15. So about 68% of children have an IQ between 85–115, 16% of 115 or more (and 16% of 85 or less), while about 2.5% have an IQ of 130 or more and 2.5% an IQ of 70 or less.

INDEX

Note: information given in a footnote is denoted by 'n.' following the page number.

Index